7 STEPS TO GET
THE FREEDOM YOU DESERVE

RAKEL CHAFIR

FREE
YOUR
BODY

To Gabby, thank you for planting a seed of faith in my heart.

TABLE OF
CONTENTS

IT ALL BEGINS
WITH A CHOICE

This book has landed in your hands for a reason.

Okay, there I said it. Cliché way to begin, no-doubt. But as I sit here, with my fingers resting on the keyboard, preparing myself to write the introduction of this book, I need you to know, right off the bat, that in this very moment you have an important choice to make—one that has the power to transform your body and your life forever. You can shut this book and forget about it. Or you can keep reading, remaining fully aware that if you follow the steps that I have put in place for you, your relationship with your body and the food on your plate will never be the same. I need you to know this now, because *I was you.* I have stood where you are standing, holding something in my hands, wondering if *this time* it will work—wondering if this is the plan, the program, the course, or the thing that will finally give me the body and the freedom I've always desired. Could this book be it?

Yes, this book is it. *Free Your Body* will show you how it is possible to get in, and stay in, the best shape of your life without endlessly dieting, fiendishly exercising, or needing to possess the willpower of a Navy Seal. In fact, all you'll need to succeed on this journey, is your willingness to follow my guidance one step at a time. If you'll do that, I promise you, that by the time you turn the last page, food and body obsession will be history.

How can you I be so sure? Because I've guided countless other women along the same exact journey on which you are about to embark. But most importantly, because I've been on this path myself.

* * *

1,725. That is the number of pounds I have gained and lost from age twelve to thirty-five. It's not a guess, but a precise calculation of the five to ten pounds I've lost and gained back with each diet, having been on approximately 10 diets per year for over two decades. Though, at some point I stopped calling them diets and switched my vocabulary to terms such as cleanses, detox programs, or nutritional plans. *Not impressed?* Let that nearly two-ton number settle in for a moment and you will be. *One-thousand seven-hundred and twenty-five pounds* is the weight of a full-size U-haul trailer, not the weight of a woman! In fact, it is more than the entire body-weight of Jon Brower Minnoch, the American man who, at his peak weight of 1,400 pounds, was the heaviest human being ever to be recorded. I am sure you'd agree, that is a lot of weight for a girl who never worn a size larger than a six! And yet, if you did the math, would you be surprised to find yourself in a similar boat (or trailer)?

Numbers have the interesting power to instantly put things into perspective. Until I added up a life-time of weight fluctuation and saw the digits 1,725 make an appearance on my calculator, all I'd ever stressed about were the two, three, five, maximum ten pounds, I'd lost and gained back over the years. *Not a big deal, right?* I was used to my weight rollercoaster. In fact, I believed that living a balanced life meant alternating between periods of discipline and self-control, and brief moments of complete indulgence. Of course, I had heard countless nutritionists and dietitians praise the notion *"everything in moderation,"* but that was never an option for me. I was all in, or all out, and despite the massive amount of stress and anxiety I experienced each day, I made it work. In fact, I had become such an expert at forcing my own body into perfect shape that I had earned the career of a successful fitness professional and nutritional coach.

Smart, strong, successful women and high-profile corporate clients filled up my classes and packed my events at some of the most elite gyms and studios in New York City and across Europe. I loved everything about my work: from inspiring women to push through their limits, to helping them feel in control, to the high I experienced watching their bodies transform before my eyes. It all came to me with tremendous ease. That is, until my own body and my own philosophies were challenged to the core—until nothing I was doing made sense anymore.

Meet me, Rakel.

"Don't worry, I'll take good care of you," my doctor said, while the nurses rolled me into the operating room. "I have done hundreds of surgeries like yours. We'll get in, repair the hernia, and you'll be as good as new."

"I hope you are right," I said. "Because nothing is ever easy when it comes to my belly."

My core has always been the most alive part of my being. It is the home of my emotions, my children, my balance, my will, my intuition—it's the doorway to my truth. So, no matter how confident my doctor was in this "simple procedure," I had a feeling that it wasn't going to be a walk in the park.

It was well past midnight when I noticed a bright light sipping through my closed eyelids.

"There you are." It was voice I recognized.

I realized that someone was holding my left hand. I tried blinking to sharpen the blurred images before me. It was Alex, my husband.

"Everything went well," he said. "There were some minor complications, but you are going to be okay… just rest now."

I tried to speak, tried to turn my head toward him, but the only thing I could do was bite my lower lip to keep myself from screaming. I felt as if someone had ripped me apart— separated my upper body from my lower limbs—and left me in two pieces unable to breathe. *What the hell happened to me? Why am I in so much pain?* I had so many questions I wanted to ask him, but I was physically unable to make a sound. With each inhale, came a sudden burst of pain so sharp it sliced through my abdomen and sent tiny bright-colored flashes in front of my eyes. Alex continued squeezing my hand. It was as if he could hear my silent screams calling for a higher dose of morphine.

"Your body had an allergic reaction," he said, as he ran his fingers through my hair, over and over again. "They can't give you any drugs until they find out what went wrong."

That moment at the hospital was the culmination of the two most intense years of my life. It began with a complicated pregnancy and severe pre-and-postpartum depression. Immediately following, I developed a vocal polyp that prevented me from teaching my classes or speaking to anyone for months, including to my three-year-old son, who didn't understand why his mommy suddenly stopped reading him bedtime stories. Next, came an unwanted relocation to Italy after nineteen years living in the United States that landed me right next-door to my parents (I had moved thousands of miles away for a reason). And now, here I was, topping it off with a choked hernia in my abdomen and its demand for immediate surgery that would, again, put me out of work and take me away from teaching for months.

"No matter what you do, keep your abdomen loose," the doctor said when he signed my discharge papers the following morning. "You don't want to pull off the internal stitches. So, no pressure and no tension in that entire area."

Seriously? I thought. *This must be a joke.* I had spent years instructing women to engage their core, fire their abs, pull their belly in, and now I was being specifically instructed to keep my own center soft and disengaged. By that point in my life, keeping my abdomen constantly activated had become second nature, an action I did instinctively a million times in a day—something I had no idea how to control.

"How do I keep my belly loose?" I asked, preoccupied.

"Just breathe and relax," he said with an easy smile, right after he told me that I wouldn't be able to move (or even pee!) on my own for weeks to come.

Relax… yeah, right.

Later that morning, a nurse wrapped a large blanket around my aching body and wheeled me and my plastic pee bag through one cold hospital corridor after another, each decorated with dull commercial prints of pastel landscapes in varying hues, out to the parking lot where Alex was waiting for me, eager to take me home.

As agonizing as it was, the ordeal of getting into the car was only a small showing of what it would be like to step down and cover the short distance that stood between the garage and the sofa in our living room. "Just leave me here. Seriously. I'll stay in the car for today!" I told him right after he'd turned off the engine. It must have taken Alex over twenty minutes to convince me that I could do it, that I could extend my legs just enough to place my feet onto the ground, that he could hold on to me, and that my body would not break apart the very moment I moved. Once we made it into the house, he carefully positioned me on the sofa where I would remain for weeks—bent over at 90 degrees, unable to stretch my legs or spine—exactly as instructed.

"The worst is over," he said, reassured to have me back at home. "Now relax."

How in the world could I relax? Forget about the surgery, the pain, and the inability to pee, I could not move and wouldn't be able to for an undetermined amount of time. This meant that for who knows how long, I could not access the very instruments I had relied on to secure my mental health, balance my mood swings, keep my sense of safety, and maintain some degree of control over my body and my life, let alone afford it.

You see, although I thought of myself as the picture of health, and made sure I always looked the part, my relationship with my body and my sense of well-being was contingent on my ability to feel in control. For over two decades, I had depended on a combination of rigorous physical discipline and strict nutrition to manage my life-long struggles with food obsession, chronic dieting, and body dysmorphia. And yet, there I was—one-hundred percent couch-bound, wounded at my core, and confined to stillness by a penetrating and constant stab right through the center of my being. All I could do was sit there and search my mind for something, anything, that would help me escape the pain and feel like myself again.

Nothing worked: Not entire seasons of *Scandal* on Netflix, not reading the uplifting words of Rupi Kaur in *Milk and Honey*, not admiring the gorgeous bouquet of pale pink roses and fluffy peonies my husband left on the coffee table next to my favorite scented candle, not hour-long phone sessions with Leah, my analyst, and not even watching my children playing in the living-room. Days went by slowly, without being able to witness any progress, until it became more and more difficult to contain the growing buildup of anxiety and depression. As I kept clicking the remote control to scan through the channels, I noticed my mind had been replaced by a carousel of ideas, each one more worrying than the last. *An injured body means no movement. No movement means no stress relief, no work, no ability to burn calories. So how would I stay thin? I'll get fat, depressed, and no one will want to work with me. My clients will move on to other healthier, happier, thinner teachers, and I'll end up doing something I hate.*

Eventually I'll feel so miserable I'll lose my husband and end up ruining my boys' lives. On my third cycle through the channels, I was ready to smash the remote.

"Fine!" I said to no one as I turned off the TV. "I can't fight it anymore. Let me feel whatever it is I am meant to feel!"

With nothing left to do but surrender, I closed my eyes and rested my hands on my wounded belly. I didn't move, didn't open my eyes, and in time, my full attention was captured by my breath. I noticed that by breathing smoothly, I could avoid coughing, sneezing, or any other sudden movement that would involuntarily recruit my abdominal muscles and make me feel like a sharp-toothed creature was eating me from the inside. And so, I stayed with that breath, striving to maintain even intervals of slow inhales and slow exhales for long uninterrupted chunks of time, which eventually turned into hours and soon days of unexpected, uninterrupted... *meditation.*

Now, meditation was something that I was familiar with, but truth be told it was not something I necessarily believed in for myself. I thought I was too busy, too active for it to "work," but for the first time, in those moments of stillness, I was able to connect with my inner silence. I am talking about the kind of thick, inner silence that would have normally spooked me; the kind I had no time for. The more absolute the silence was, the stronger its healing effects. I'm sure you've heard people speak of it, the place of intuitive hits, spiritual downloads, divine guidance, and sometimes visions. I never thought it could happen to someone as skeptical as myself, but it was in that silence that I heard it for the first time.

You have a choice.

It was an internal, intuitive voice that spoke to me straight from my gut. At first, I dismissed it, paying no attention to what I had heard, firm on my belief that divine guidance has to be some kind of product of peoples' imagination, and definitely not a product of mine. I chose to keep focusing on my breathing, my physical healing, but the voice came to me again.

Choose you, it said. *Choose yourself.*

Don't you see I am trying to breathe here? I silently responded, now feeling both foolish and more than a little annoyed.

Choose yourself, it said, again, with unquestionable clarity. *Now. Exactly as you are.*

Choose me... now? Exactly as I am? It made no sense. How could I choose myself when I felt so lost, depressed, when I was cemented into a ninety-degree position, in constant pain, and attached to a pee bag? The only times I had ever felt good enough to possibly consider the idea of "choosing me," were in the brief moments that followed an achievement of some kind. When I deserved it, like when I saw a thinner image of my body reflected in the mirror, when I impeccably completed a detox program to the very end, or when I received some kind of recognition for an outstanding performance. Choosing, me, now, exactly as I was—completely wrecked—was insane.

Choose you. Still, the voice kept tormenting me in my couch-bound meditations. *You are enough. Everything you want in your life will come with that awareness. Choose You.* I wanted to scream, but as I kept breathing, with my eyes closed, I visualized myself standing at a crossroads. Perhaps, on a deeper level, I still had the power to make a choice. And maybe, just maybe, the act of choosing me had nothing to do with the circumstances I was in or with things I could accomplish. I *could* choose to take the path I knew best. Force myself through this experience until I could return to full-on fix-mode. Or I could choose a new path. Stop fighting what was happening to me and choose to connect *now* to a version of myself that existed despite the pain in my belly and the wounds in my broken body.

"*Okay*," I finally said, still feeling awkward entertaining the idea of having an internal dialogue with some kind of higher power. "*I choose... myself. I choose me.*"

With my eyes still closed, I said those words again and again. As I repeated that mantra, I began to feel a tingling sensation creep up my arms and into my chest, followed by an unexpected wash of relief. The physical pain was not gone by any means, but my resistance to feeling the pain had lifted. I was in my body without attempting to fix it, judge it, control it, ignore it, or define it. I was in it, owning that moment fully. Understanding, for the very first time, that what I really wanted—besides getting back on my feet and going out for a much-needed glass of wine (ok... maybe two)—was to show up fully in my life, feeling free in my body without having to renounce staying fit for the rest of my life.

Could I possibly do that?

The answer turned out to be yes. All I had to do was have the courage to choose myself and be willing to take one step at the time. And so, I did. I listened to that inner guidance, and I placed one foot in front of the other, day after day, until I discovered there were seven steps that would take me down a new path. It was that path that allowed me to turn my desires into reality. Yes, my body recovered in time, and no, I didn't lose my clients, my marriage, or my boys. But it was the inner healing that I received on that sofa that was far greater than I could have ever imagined.

I was finally able to understand what it was like to live freely in my body, and it changed *everything* about how I worked with other women. I wanted them to feel what life was like in a body they loved without the need for rigorous workouts, routine fasts, and weight loss programs. I had been so deeply moved and transformed by what I had a chance to experience myself, that I felt called to share what I began to my Forever Fit and Free process with my clients—women of all ages, cultural backgrounds, and body types—whom now, just like me, get to be feel free and look their absolute best. Their stories became a testament to what is possible, and the very motivation that inspired me to write this book and make these teachings available to all. That's right. Now it's your turn.

You see, *you* are the reason for this book. You have inspired me to put down on paper all the lessons, the tools, and the stories that have changed the bodies and lives of the countless women I have worked with in the last three years. I want you to experience this transformational change, too.

HERE IS THE PLAN FOR OUR WORK TOGETHER

In the coming pages, I'll teach you something that every diet book you have ever read lacks—an effective seven-step system for working through your emotional, physical, and psychological blocks, so that you won't need to keep willing, forcing, fighting, and dieting yourself into shape. With each chapter, I will introduce you to a new step and give you access to the very tools and exercises I have used myself and with my clients. You can work this seven-step process as slow or as fast as you desire as long as you feel complete with each step before moving onto the next. Don't worry about how long it will take you to get the last step, because as soon as you begin to practice choosing yourself and diving into the support work that I have included at the end of each chapter, you will know what the right rhythm is for *you*.

Each chapter in this book represents one step forward on our journey together. It might be tempting to skip ahead to see what each chapter is about, but I encourage you—because it really won't work if you don't—to start by reading the first chapter and then taking the time you need to complete the Support Work for the first chapter. Each chapter is followed by work that supports the lesson, and that work is just as important as reading this book from beginning to end.

But because I know that some of you are curious, here's a peak into the 7 Steps.

THE 7 STEPS TO FREE YOUR BODY

Step 1: In this step, I will show you exactly why no diet has ever worked for you in the long run and why all the good intentions, affirmations, and positive thinking in the world will never heal your relationship to food and body image unless you make the one choice that will change your life forever.

Step 2: Here, you will learn that you do not have to wait for anything or anyone to get the body you desire and the freedom you deserve. In fact, in this step, I will show you exactly how to restore your power and give yourself permission to transform your body and your life one moment at a time.

Step 3: Get ready to unearth your own unique process for long-term success. Understand the connection between feeling supported and feeling full, and discover how choosing yourself will always guide you to the next right action.

Step 4: You can't lose weight for good, but you can release it forever. On this step, I will show you how to release the emotional weight that is keeping you from feeling and looking your absolute best.

Step 5: By the time you get here, you'll know how to use the power of choice to bounce back into your commitment to free your body, as well as let go of what doesn't serve you. You will learn how to experience emptiness and normalize empty space inside and outside your stomach.

Step 6: Get ready to move from theory and spirituality straight into science. In this step, I will show you how to rewire your brain, create biological change, and form new behavioral patterns that will allow you to beat the cravings and restore your self-regulating abilities.

Step 7: By the time you arrive here, you'll be ready for an all new level of growth. In fact, you will understand, on a visceral level, that living freely in the best shape of your life is not about controlling your impulses, or being impeccable, but rather allowing yourself to feel fully satisfied and open to welcoming in what you so deeply desire.

Sound like a lot? Don't worry. In the final chapter, you will learn how to put all seven steps together and turn the Forever Fit and Free process into your go-to strategy to bounce back quickly any time you need or want to.

THE SUPPORT WORK SECTION

There is something else I want you to know before you take the first step. *I care about you.* I would actually put an F-word between the "I" and the "care" to express how I truly feel about each woman I get to work with, but my editor tells me is best avoid cursing to that degree so soon, not to mention that I have no desire to be disrespectful to anyone. So, I'll keep it kosher for you. But know that I have infused this book with the intention of you feeling my support each step of the way. I will be right there by your side, because I have been where you are. And because I care about you, I want you to do the work that delivers the results, which is precisely why I have created the Support Work section at the end of each chapter. I want you to integrate each step into your life and make it your own.

I can't stress this enough: If you skip the integration, all you will have from this book is a bunch of information but no real transformation. And I want more for you.

I want you to Free Your Body for the rest of your life.

So that you know what to expect in the coming pages, here are the three exercises you will find at the end of each chapter in your support work section:

Your Power Statement: This exercise calls for you to witness your inner dialogue, so that you can familiarize yourself with the beliefs about your body that are driving your life experience. I will invite you to write a specific statement that reflects the lesson included in the preceding chapter which you will begin to use in your daily life as a powerful mantra that will instantly reconnect you to your truth whenever you feel misaligned.

Your Foundation: Here, you will have the opportunity to rebuild your home base, what you choose to believe about yourself and your body. After each step of this journey, as you will gain a better understanding of yourself and your desires, you'll add-on to *Your Foundation*, and thus begin to slowly create a new map to navigate your life.

Your action: The final component of each support work section is the action work. By following my suggestion to take small yet powerful actions in your relationship to food, you will bring your awareness to the table and shift the way you relate to nurturing yourself one step at the time. Together with the internal awakenings you experience in each step, *Your Action* will bring forth miraculous shifts in the way you look and feel.

THE TRUE YOU

Our journey together will be intense, but not quite in the way you might be thinking—not in the specific meal plans or grueling exercises or fast twice-per-week kind of way. You see, I have no interest in helping you lose the ten, twenty, or even forty pounds that you will most likely regain within the year. Instead, I will show you how to stop forcing yourself into the body of your dreams and how to allow your absolute best body and life to become the inevitable byproducts of *your choices*. Or, better yet, *seven specific choices* that have the power to bring forth permanent body-and-mind transformation no matter how old, heavy, active, or inactive you may be in this very moment. Your success on this journey will depend entirely on your willingness and your ability to put you—*the true you*—before the very outcomes you desire.

When I say *true you*, I'm not taking about the *you* who broke the diet, gained the weight, experienced the traumas, or made a series of bad decisions, but the part of *you* that still is and forever will be *whole*. I am referring to the innocent version of yourself you were born with, whom you have likely forgotten, but who nonetheless continues to live beneath the layers of who you have become over the years. I like to call that part of you *the angel in the stone*, an expression I borrowed from the most famous artist of the Italian renaissance, Michelangelo.

When Michelangelo spoke about his creative process as a sculptor, he used to say he saw an angel trapped within the stone, fully present in all her glorious beauty. All he did, was chip away the marble, layer after layer, until he could set her free. That simple yet powerful description, moved me to my core. It reminded me that the free and powerful version of ourselves is already there. She has just been trapped under thick layers of old stories and limiting beliefs, and she is waiting patiently for you to dismantle the stone and let her out.

As I told you from the first page, you have picked up this book for a reason. *You* heard the call of *the angel* trapped within the stone. And just like I was on that first day, when heard that inner guidance asking me to choose myself and calling me into a new path, you are now the one standing at a crossroads. You can place this book back where you found it, or you can choose yourself, buckle up, breath in deep, and take the first, brave step to free your body. If you choose to say, and I sure hope you do, get excited and prepare yourself to witness the most miraculous changes in your body and your life. That is a promise.

CHOOSE
YOU

"How long have you been feeling this way?"

"Forever," I said without hesitation as I stretched my legs over the brand-new, creamy leather lounge chair in Dr. Logan's office, a chair that molded so perfectly around the frame of my body, I almost forgot about the $250 I had just charged to my Visa for one single session of hypnosis.

"I know it might feel that way, but there has to be a moment when it all started," she continued. "Do you remember the very first time you felt bad about your body?

"I was five, I think. It was the morning of my fifth birthday."

"Then, let's try to go back there."

Here we go...the inner child crap again! I thought to myself, unimpressed by her suggestion.

That was the first time I tried hypnosis. The first time I willingly attempted to relive the very moment food and body obsession began to take hold on my life, and no, I didn't think it would work in a million years. Nonetheless, I was willing to try anything. I was twenty-two years old, going through a painful breakup, and so depressed I couldn't find a reason to get out of bed in the morning. I had stopped going to classes, stopped showing up at work, and now I had maxed out my last active credit card. Irrational as it may sound, I was in the depths of my quarter life crises. I was certain that if I was a size zero, then everything else in my life would be perfect. If I was thinner, my boyfriend would still be with me, or I'd be one of those girls who gets spotted walking out of a local coffee shop and asked to audition for a major motion picture, or I'd run right into the man of my dreams who would change my life forever.

Unfortunately, no matter how much weight I lost or how hard I had tried to look the part of the woman who gets it all, my skeptical ass still landed on that comfy leather chair, listening to a soothing and soft voice wrapped in a thick British accent, asking me to close my eyes, put my judgments on pause, relax, and start counting backward from 300. Which, if you haven't tried, by the way, is trickier than you may think.

"Two hundred eighty-five, two hundred eighty… four, two hundred eighty-three, two…"

"Where are you now?" she asked, tapping my right shoulder—an indication that I should fall into an even deeper state of relaxation.

"I'm in Mom's bathroom."

"Can you tell me what you are doing there?"

"I'm climbing on top of Mom's dresser, the one that faces the mirror, so that I can see myself."

"What's on your mind in this moment?"

"I can't wait to see how tall I am..." I said, diving into the mix of pride and wonder I felt on that day, anticipating the image of a tall, pretty, five-year-old girl who was finally old enough to start ballet.

"What happens next?"

"I'm on the dresser, and I stand up tall, to see my myself in the mirror... and... "

No words. I suddenly couldn't speak. My heart leaped into my throat and I lost access to my voice.

"Tell me, Rakel, what do you see?" she said, pulling the words out of my mouth.

"I see... my thighs... my thighs are so thick," I said breathing hard, clutching the arms of the chair. "They rub together almost all the way down to my knees. I am fat, ugly… nothing like a ballerina."

"Breathe, Rakel… Breathe. You are doing great." She was tapping on my right shoulder again. "What do you do next?"

"I bend my knees, reach both my hands behind me, then I grab my inner thighs to pull the extra skin all the way back so I can see the reflection of the slender girl I wish I was. I would look so much better, if only I had a gap between my thighs. Then…"

"Then what?"

"Then I see my mom. She is standing by the door, looking at me. I pull my hands away, straighten my legs as fast as I can, but…"

"But what?"

"She is standing there looking at me with a grin on her face, and I… I am mortified, frozen… *Please, God, make her walk away… pretend she didn't see me.* I'm praying, silently. But she doesn't. She just stands there, waiting for me to look up."

"'What are you doing up there?' I remember my mom saying. 'And why in the world are you wearing that body suit? It's so tight on you.'"

"What do *you* say?"

"Nothing. I look down to study the shape of my feet as she keeps talking about some dress I should wear... all I can do is hold my breath and try not to cry. Finally, she stops talking and she walks out closing the bathroom door behind her."

"So, what do you do?"

"I sit down on the dresser and cry. I try not to make a sound. *I'm fat. I need to fix my body. Or I can't be a dancer, ever. And I'll never be happy, or loved. Not even by my mother.*"

"I see..." she whispered, tapping one last time on my right shoulder.

"Now, Rakel, try to visualize yourself as you are now, an adult, standing in that bathroom, next to your five-year-old self. What do you think she needs to hear from you?"

Crickets. I searched my mind for something to say but found nothing. Don't get me wrong, by that point in my life, I had done my share of self-help work. I'd been on painful play dates with my inner child and I'd written her a bunch of love letters. Not to mention, I'd practiced positive affirmations of all kinds, and I knew that repeating the usual *you are beautiful, smart, thin, pretty, kind, and lovable* would not cut it *for me*. What I didn't know, was why those things didn't work as promised. With so many success stories showing countless happy endings, providing evidence that other women were able to transform their lives and their bodies thanks to magical affirmations and past regressions, the conclusion I had come to was that *I had to be the problem*. I was the girl who, after a successful diet, would regain the weight back and have to start all over. I was the girl who ended up feeling miserable and insecure no matter how hard I tried. I was to blame.

And yet, despite all the self-help books I had read, and the countless healing workshops I had attended, I was missing one important piece of information. Whether we are five years old or forty, we cannot just tell ourselves that we are beautiful, loved, smart, or in any way better than who we actually believe we are. I mean we *can*, but it won't be effective unless we can also feel those words within every cell of our body. The Universe doesn't respond to English, or any other foreign languages for that matter (trust me I have tried a few), it responds to vibration. Therefore, in order to cause any real transformation, we must use more than words. We must believe, and literally vibrate, with whatever it is we are saying, which is far from easy to do when your present circumstances and your current feelings appear to stand in direct opposition with the words coming out of our mouth. No matter how many times we repeat those affirmations out loud, the dreams we have and the things we want to achieve cannot be forced into reality by fixing what appears to be imperfect, or by convincing ourselves that we are any better than we truly believe ourselves to be.

However—and this is the groundbreaking news—there is an even better version of who we wish we could be, and how we wish we could look, that can and will evolve as the byproduct of choosing ourselves. To choose yourself, you don't need to have positive affirmations at hand, the right body, or any special powers of self-acceptance that allow you to appreciate the way you look at any given moment. All you need, is the willingness to make a decision and to put *you* before the very outcomes you desire. You, before your ideal weight, your fit body, and your perfect life. Choose yourself and allow those desires to evolve as the natural byproduct of who you are. When you do that, you choose to put your *true* Self first, *everything* changes. In other words, you shift into alignment.

You are the gatekeeper of your own gate.
With the right alignment, everything you want
makes its way into your experience.
—Hester Hicks

BUILDING AN ALLIANCE

According to the Oxford English Dictionary, the word *alignment* originated in late eighteenth Century France from the verb *aligner*. While one definition of the word describes alignment as "arrangement in a straight line," a second bestows upon us a most powerful notion, "a position of agreement or alliance."

Only by aligning what we desire with what we believe we can receive, are we able to bring clarity into our bodies and minds and move forward with ease. You see, if you desire to get in shape and effortlessly live in a fit body, you must also believe that desire is available to you, and that you deserve to have that experience in your life. If you don't find that alignment, the internal contradiction will inevitably reflect your external circumstances and lead you to experience roller coaster results, self-sabotage, and all kinds of emotional ups and down.

This notion of alignment, or agreement, between our desires and our beliefs is incredibly powerful, and it is also the reason why the many diets you have been on and the countless programs you have signed up for have eventually failed you. On the one hand you have committed to do whatever it takes to get a fit body that can make you feel beautiful, worthy, and in control. On the other, you remained attached to the belief that you are broken, damaged, and somehow destined to always be on a diet and never at peace with your body. *Can you see the contradiction—the misalignment?*

The moment you choose yourself —unbound by any specific condition— you access the power to mend that incongruity, because you rise above it. And each time you repeat that choice, you strengthen the alliance between your heartfelt desires and your ability to receive them. The stronger the bond you create within you, the greater the transformation you can witness outside yourself.

Meet Casey.

Born and raised in a middle-class family in suburban Chicago, Casey joined my eight-week Transformation program on her fortieth birthday, driven by the desire to lose the eighteen pounds she had gained after she quit smoking the previous year. She had been on and off all kinds of diets since she was fourteen, and over the course of her adult life had signed up for a plethora of fitness programs, meal delivery plans, and gym memberships, without ever being able to obtain long-term results. Casey alternated between her "skinny years" and "chubby years" (as she liked to call them), and by the time we met, there was no doubt in her mind that being fat was in her DNA and that she would always have to work extra hard to fight against her unfair destiny. Still, she was on a mission to drop the eighteen pounds she had gained, plus an extra five to ten, even if it meant that maybe she should start smoking again.

"I understand that you want to lose weight, and I am not saying I won't help you do that," I said to her at our first session. "But let me ask you something. What would happen if I told you that in order to get permanent results, you had to stop feeling the need to fix your body?"

"You don't understand," she instantly responded, looking at me perplexed. "I can't. I'd gain a ridiculous amount of weight. I'd get too far out of control. And besides, I wouldn't even know how…"

"Let's just pretend you knew how… that you *could* do it. What do you think would happen then?"

"I just told you. I'd lose control…*I'd* probably get morbidly obese and die depressed and alone."

Casey was frustrated by such preposterous questions. Why weren't we getting down to business, setting some goals down on paper, taking measurements, and talking about meal plans?

"What if instead of losing control, getting morbidly obese and dying depressed and alone, you could be free from dieting *and* still get in the best shape of your life?" I continued. "Just saying, what if giving up that preoccupation to fix the way you look could help you release all the weight you desire and look better than you ever did?"

Casey looked at me as if I had just asked her to convert to an unknown faith that demanded she move to Nepal and give up all her possessions. I was not, of course, trying to do that, but I was asking her to reframe her faith in her body and in her life. As you can imagine, her resistance was palpable. You see, when you have spent your entire life on a mission to fix yourself—relentlessly trying to conquer all that is wrong with your body—the very idea that you don't actually need to control anything can feel as bizarre as someone suddenly suggesting you convert to a new religion. Or me telling you that you no longer need to pay your taxes by April 15. In fact, let's go as far as imagining that I told you that you'll never have to pay your taxes again. *That bizarre.*

Casey was stuck in a loop that spun her from feeling terrible, defeated, and fat (her *chubby years*) to feeling strong enough to master a temporary solution to get close to what she wanted (her *skinny years*). Around, and around, and around in this loop, a loop that I am pretty sure you have at times inhabited, where everything is either up or down, black or white, good or bad—thin or fat. Unless Casey hustled, sacrificed, and worked her ass off, she would be destined to fulfill her self-inflicted prophecy and become a lethargic depressed woman destined to die fat and alone. Therefore, each time Casey gained a pound or skipped a workout, she would slide closer to what she had internally accepted as her destiny, and each time she got into a new diet or completed a physical challenge, she would lose herself in a short-lived high. No matter how many times she lost weight or how hard she worked on her goals, her personal history of periodical highs and lows had turned her life into a map that looped Casey back around to that same old story again and again and again. *I am destined to be fat.*

Casey's only chance to break free from her condition was to witness her lack of alignment between what she was trying to achieve and what she believed she could have. Only then, would she be able to step outside that never-ending diet loop and take a first powerful step into her Forever Fit and Free journey. That is why, no matter how resistant she was during our first week working together, I wasn't going to send her off with yet another diet program and exercise-chart she could easily get from any personal trainer who would charge her a fraction of my prices. I was determined to help her see that she needed to mend that internal contradiction and open up to the idea that there could be a better way.

"Even if what you say could be possible, I wouldn't even know where to start."

"You would start by choosing you," I said. "That is the first thing you need to do."

"Choose me? How? How do I choose myself when I look so fat? I don't get that."

"Well, to begin, I am in no way asking you to abandon your eighteen-pound objective. I am asking you to reframe it and shift the way you relate to your desires. I can show you how to get in the absolute best shape of your life, but that cannot be a condition to feeling good enough about yourself. That is the only way to get permanent results. And whether you believe me or not, I know for certain, you can get there. The moment you choose *you*, you give yourself full permission to pursue whatever you desire without the pressure and the anxiety of needing to prove yourself along the way. That freedom, right there, will instantly make you far more powerful and effective in every area of your life, including when it comes to releasing body weight."

"So, that's it? I put myself first?" Casey asked, beginning to see that there might be value in what I was suggesting, but still feeling reluctant to believe the solution to her lifelong struggle could begin with something so basic as making a choice.

"Yes. That's it. That's the first step. It's simple. But that doesn't mean it'll be easy."

For decades, Casey had identified herself with the story of a woman who would need to spend her entire life stressing over food and working relentlessly to fix herself. That narrative had played in her head for so long that she couldn't possibly imagine her life without it. And yet, there I was, asking her to witness that story and recognize it for what it truly was —nothing more than a thought she repeated over and over in her head—a thought that contradicted her desires and constantly pulled her away from the body and life she deserved to experience.

CHOOSE YOU

Now, before you get all, "Oh here we go again with the stories and limiting beliefs," which I know is something that has become somewhat like a modern maxim for self-improvement work these days, hear me out: I'm not here to replace beliefs with positive affirmations or dismantle them through inner child meditations (though I'm not knocking either). I am here to tell you that, you, just like Casey, are standing at a cross-roads with a choice to make. You can stay on the same loop you have been on until now, jump into the next diet cycle and do it again and again and again for the rest of your days, or you can choose yourself, enter uncharted territory, and take your first step forward on the path towards a fit and free future.

Which direction you take will depend entirely on your willingness to put your *Self* above all things, including the very things that you have believed to be true about your character, your history, and your body up until this moment. Like I once said to Casey, it's simple, but it will not be easy. In fact, in a way, it will feel much like leaving home to move to a place you've never been before, one that sounds unpredictable and too good to be true.

When we visit my parents in Italy (I'm Italian, by the way) my son William and I like to take long walks in the woods, which runs all along the coast. Each time it's like entering into our own little magic world, where we can pick blackberries, find treasures, spot pixie dust coming out of a bush or even a pointy red hat behind a tree. My intention during those walks is always the same: let our imaginations run wild. Yet even in those moments, when we laugh and whisper secrets to each other, there is always something firm on my mind—to give my child a sense of direction, help him identify specific spots on our path, so that one day, if he ever finds himself alone or lost, he can use the visual reference points I taught him, to safely return home, to me.

"See Mrs. Silvana's fruit stand at the bottom of the hill?" I say, pointing ahead. "It's the only one covered in purple Morning Glories, and that's how you know where to make your turn." We walk for a bit longer, and then again, I open my mouth. "Look! It's the long and skinny walkway framed by large pines, and that proud olive tree standing at the intersection of the *Viale*. That's Grandma's road, right?" He nods. "Remember, you have to pass four homes before you get to her garden. Let's count them together…" And we do.

Just like that, I have given my son a visual map, one I'm pretty sure he will keep firm in his mind forever. That is what parents do, right? They make sure we have a set of directions to navigate not just the trails by the seaside, but throughout life—to keep us safe and allow us to always find our way home and back to them. Such is the function of our core belief system. Like a map, filled with stories and points of reference that help us return to what feels most safe and predictable, our belief system helps us navigate life and experience certainty in a world that feels otherwise intangible and unsafe.

As sad as it may sound and feel, hearing and ultimately believing "you are too fat to be a dancer," "being fat is in your DNA," or "you will always need to be on a diet," does serve some kind of purpose in life. No matter what happens around us or to us, we can always go back to feeling fat and ashamed, and obsessing about the food we could eat or should not eat, because the familiarity of all of that leaves us feeling far less lost, lonely or scared than anything uncertain.

On the contrary, choosing to abandon those points of reference asks us to dive into a foreign place, travel without a map, and leave the familiar and the expected. Think about it, life is unpredictable, and we can't possibly know for certain if tomorrow we'll still have a job, if our partner will be faithful, or if gas will be affordable. Hell, we can't even know for certain if we'll still be alive! There is, however, something that we can always count on if and when tomorrow comes—that we'll be able to stress over the missing gap of our inner thighs, what we should or should not have for lunch, or how many calories we'll need to burn to feel good. So, I get it. Choosing to go on as just you, without that map of reference points, is scary to say the least.

But what if I told you that the path to be forever fit, the one without that map you have acquired along the way, is deeply satisfying and filled with miracles? *Could that be the case?*

Chances are, like Casey and most women, your relationship with your body and the food on your plate has long been interconnected with specific reference points—effort, conditions, requirements, rules you get to follow or break, and results you get to achieve or never obtain—on a path that has been strenuous, draining, and void of ease, freedom, beauty, and enjoyment. Believing that living fit is impossible without massive effort, specific rules, and major self-restraint can feel so real in our minds that letting go of that belief would sound just as implausible as permanent tax exemption. And yet, unlike taxes (which after reading this book you will still have to pay... I know...*bummer!*) I am here to show you that you can stop buying into the life-sucking convictions that have consumed you for so long, create a new and real sense of safety, and find your own alignment.

The key to fully understanding and benefiting from the lesson in this chapter—which I promise can, and *will*, change your body and your life—lies in your willingness to reframe those points of reference and understand that getting and staying in the best shape of your life *cannot* be a consequence of taxing effort, persistent willpower, or any other external circumstance. At least, not if you want to maintain those results for decades to come. In fact, when our desire is to free your body and stay in shape *forever* and not *temporarily* lose weight, unshakable willpower and willingness to work your ass off (as many of us have demonstrated to possess) won't do the job. On this journey, the key to our success is not in *what* we do, or *how hard* we are willing to work to get there. It is entirely *the why*—the purpose behind each choice we make, including what we choose to eat and how we choose to move. To free your body, that *why* must be to honor your *Self* above all things.

It took Casey a few weeks to get used to this notion, but when she could finally get a feel for what it meant to choose herself, she decided to start by adding just one new reference point and making that her non-negotiable—joy. Every action, from that point had to bring her joy, and that included every meal and every exercise. By choosing herself and making joy a priority in her life, Casey was able to shift the *why* behind her actions and take a first step onto an alternative path that allowed her to witness incredible shifts in the way she felt about herself and her life—lighter, happier, and worthy of what she desired.

Thanks to her one, new reference point, Casey soon discovered her passion for outdoor hiking and hot yoga, as well as a keen interest in studying the philosophy of Ayurveda. Not surprisingly, the changes Casey made in her mindset and lifestyle soon reflected a slender, healthier, and stronger body that she felt proud of and grateful for. And from there, it only got better. Next, she discovered a passion for cooking, signed up for a series of classes, and connected with a new group of people who shared her same interests in life, including her now fiancée. All of that and more came as a consequence of choosing herself and shifting the *why* behind her actions.

I know what you are thinking... sounds too easy. Really, I get it. Choosing yourself doesn't sound as challenging or extraordinary as a forty-day liquid-only cleanse or training for a triathlon, but trust me, it's the most ambitious path you can choose for yourself. We are not talking about doing something restrictive or backbreaking for a certain amount of time, we are talking about having the courage to step into the unknown, to resist the seduction of fixing ourselves, and choosing to dive deep into a journey that will change our bodies and lives *forever*. And here is the thing. It's a million percent worth it.

This first step, choosing yourself, is first for a reason. Until you are able to recognize and release the old points of reference that have kept your food and body obsession alive until today, you won't be in the position to change the *why* behind your actions and create a powerful alliance between what you want and what you believe you can receive. But once you establish that alignment, you will be able to start moving full-force towards the body and life you have always desired, without having to fight your way through each step or confining yourself into a loop.

Just like Casey, whom last time I heard from had dropped three dress sizes—without being on a diet— I never turned my back on my commitment to choose myself. Whenever thoughts about my body or food start to accelerate inside my head and spin out of control, I Choose Me. And now, with this book —you can have the same opportunity. It doesn't matter how many times you have failed at dieting, how heavy or how old you are in this moment, what you do for living, how many children you carried and delivered, what your parents look like, what they told you, how much money you make, or what terrible traumas or injuries you have experienced. None of that can prevent you from taking this step, because you, all on your own, have all that is required to create an alliance between what you want and what you believe you can receive.

I know you may not see it yet, but as I told you in the introduction, you have picked up this book for a reason, you heard the call of *the* angel, you have sensed she is in there, trapped within the stone, and you are ready to set her free. If you weren't, trust me, you'd be reading something else right now. *This book* in your hands is your sculptor's tool box. All you need to do is be willing to make the seven choices, one step at the time, and complete the support work at the end of each chapter with an open mind and open heart, because there is no wrong way to walk this path as long as you walk it. Trust that your willingness is all you need to take this step. Because no matter who you are or how insecure you feel, there is only one absolute truth. *You are more than your current body weight, more than your perception of you self, more than all judgments and opinions you heard over the years, including your own. All you got to do to see it, is* give yourself permission to be who you already are beneath the layers of limiting beliefs that are keeping you in the dark. The free, powerful woman, ready to choose herself and shine bright.

Looking back on that day in the lounge, the day when I was willing to dive into that memory that marked the beginning of the abusive relationship I had established with my body, I know now exactly what to say. I would sit by my five-year-old self as she cried on that dresser and tell her the same exact thing that I'll say to you now. "Choose you, and not because your thighs are thin enough, but because you are so much more than your thighs. You, the light that lives within you, is what this world needs most. That light can make you dance, grow, teach, fly, write, cook, travel, find the love of your life, or do whatever it is you want to do. So, go on, choose yourself, and shine bright!"

May this first step initiate your journey to a free body and a miraculous life.

SUPPORT WORK

POWER STATEMENT

*Write down the following power statement
and repeat it as often as you can.*

**"I choose me, because I am more than anyone's
opinion or perception, including my own."**

Repeat this statement to yourself or out loud whenever you
experience a less than ideal moment during the day, so that
you can strengthen the habit of placing who *You* are before
any random negative thought about yourself and your body.
For instance, you may catch yourself thinking "I can't believe my thighs are so thick." or "I look fat and unattractive."
That is when you'd stop, acknowledge there is an opportunity
to choose, take a deep, clearing breath and tell yourself: **"I
choose me, because I more than anyone's opinion or
perception, including my own."** Or maybe, you just had
a difficult day and ended up eating far too many sweets, so
much so that you now feel bloated and uncomfortable. Right

there, as you feel the sudden rise of frustration, anxiety, depression, or resentment towards yourself, you'd stop whatever it is you are doing, recognize the presence of an opportunity to choose, and repeat to yourself: "I choose me, because I more than anyone's opinion or perception, including my own."

It will only take you a moment—the time it takes to repeat your Power Statement—but that moment will be extremely powerful, and it will help you shift your behavior without attempting to control it or fix it.

YOUR FOUNDATION

Take five minutes to finish the following sentence.

I choose to believe that I am

_____

_____

_____

Your main goal for this exercise is to create alignment—to align what you desire for yourself with what you believe you can receive or accomplish. Remember, in order to be successful, you cannot live with an internal contradiction. Make your foundation short, quick and believable to you. All it needs to do is make you feel even a little better. For example, you may have a hard time working with, "I choose to believe that my body looks toned and gorgeous," but you could possibly align with more ease with something like, "I choose to believe I am on the right path and each day I am getting closer and closer to freeing my body forever."

Once you've written a statement that feels good to you, copy it down onto an index card, a piece of paper, or on your phone. Make sure you read it frequently, but at least once first thing in the morning, and once last thing at night.

TAKE ACTION

*Use the following guideline
each time you are having a meal.*

**Eat whatever you want, and as much as you want,
as long as you are truly hungry.**

Not thirsty, not angry, not lonely, not bored, not fatigued, not frustrated. Only if you are physically hungry. Whenever you get the idea to eat, stop for a moment and ask yourself: *Am*

I truly hungry for food? If the answer is yes, go ahead and eat. However, if you notice that you are just craving something, looking for emotional comfort, needing something to do with your hands or your time, stop. Pick up your journal, or your phone, then respond to this question: *What do I need in this moment that I am trying to replace with food?*

Write and breathe until the craving begins to subside. *If you still feel the need to eat after that, give yourself permission to do so without guilt or shame.*

Change is on its way.

CHOOSE
NOW

All she ever wanted was a fairy godmother, a pair of sparkly glass slippers, a handsome prince ready to save her and love her forever, and a dreamy ball gown to waltz the night away. Now, tell the truth, at least at some point in your life, didn't you want exactly the same thing? Come on Girl! Not even the shoes?

Well, *I sure did.*

When I first reunited with that old book, I was two days shy of turning thirty-nine, and way past my wannabe-princess phase. Yet, the very moment I laid my eyes on it, I suddenly felt grateful for taking on Mom's basement revamping project and forgot all about having given away my first day off in over a month. There it was, my once upon a time, most beloved possession, buried at the bottom of a large box that contained my entire childhood. Tutus, carnival costumes, my first pair of point shoes, my tennis racket, my precious Michael Jackson tape collection... and *Cinderella.* Its bright colors were faded and the edges worn, but as soon as I held that book in my hands, I was a little girl again, getting ready for the ball where I'd meet my prince and my life would change forever.

That night, *Cinderella* in hand, I snuggled in bed with my two children, one on each side of my tired body—better than any butterfly cocoon.

"Look!" I said to William, barely able to contain my excitement as I readied myself to open the book to the first page. "This was Mommy's favorite book when she was your age."

William took a quick look at the "girly" cover and then without saying a word, he grabbed his new Transformer from the side table and began to manipulate the bionic figure, turning it into a truck. Meanwhile Donovan, the baby, was busy operating the light switch on the headboard, intrigued by the magic *on* and *off* ability of our chandelier. Still, I cracked open my precious book to its first page and began reading the story out loud—to myself.

Undisturbed by my boys' lack of consideration, I read *Cinderella* cover to cover. But it didn't evoke the same feelings it once did. In fact, I was upset by the message that came through. My whole life, I had thought of *Cinderella* as the magic tale of a girl who overcomes evil with kindness after years of neglect and unfairness. But now, all I could see was a young woman who never stood up for herself, never got to express her feelings, and never had the freedom to respond to continuous verbal and emotional abuse. In fact, if it wasn't for Mr. Prince Charming, by the time the clock struck midnight, Cinderella would have gone back to her attic, where she'd sleep on a torn mattress surrounded by friendly rats and end up working as a slave until her last breath. Thankfully the young girl was skinny, beautiful, well-dressed, and basically perfect at everything from singing to housekeeping, so it was only a matter of time before she'd get a real chance at life. One dance, to charm the prince, be saved, and live *happily ever after.*

How could I have failed to see the trap concealed beneath the sweet, gift-wrapped ending, which Cinderella shares with all respectable fairytales I have ever loved? This apparently innocent story I have worshipped since I was a toddler has taught girls like myself to disconnect from the imperfect present to fantasize about how one significant event in our future—in this case meeting the guy of our dreams at a ball—would lead to a more than a perfect life filled with everlasting romance, joy, happiness, and security. And just like that, the notion of placing our lives on hold until the day the stars align in the sky and all things suddenly turn in our favor had infiltrates our psyches, not to mention, our bodies.

Ever heard anyone say, "When I'll lose the last ten… twenty… forty… pounds, I will start dating?" Or "Once I get through this holiday season, I will eat healthy and exercise every day." "When I look decent in a dress, I'll buy myself something I truly love." "When I finish this diet, I'll get to enjoy food." "When I have a baby, I'll feel complete." "When I lose the baby weight, I'll feel like a woman again." "When I get in shape, my life will be easier."

There is an underlining message behind every single one of those statements.

Once I *fill   in the blank* , then I'll get to… *take care of myself, enjoy life, feel worthy, eat healthy, discover what kind of exercise I truly love, go for what I want in life…* In other words, once I get the perfect body and control my eating, then, and only then, will I live *happily ever after.*

This "happily ever after" message is detrimental in relationships of all kinds; however, when it comes to the way we relate to our body and food, it's particularly insidious. Whenever we get locked onto the idea of a perfect future, our actions, our lifestyle choices, and the way we care and feel about ourselves and our bodies becomes entirely dependent on an external element. In other words, we dissociate from our reality (the only place we have available to create real change and cause real transformation) to fantasize about a yet inexistent moment in the future where we'll get to be thin enough and disciplined enough to deserve that happy ending all girls dream of.

In truth however, until we choose to tune into the now—not the fantasy future of happy endings—we remain unable to take empowering actions for ourselves or get the fit body we desire and the freedom we deserve.

Your greatest self has been waiting your whole life;
don't make it wait any longer.
—Steve Maraboli

HAPPILY EVER AFTER

When I searched the web for a definition of "happy ending" the first one I found was *a cliché*d conclusion, in which all loose ends are tied up and all main characters are content. Another "happy ending" was more interesting or risqué (well, I'll let you judge for yourself). "A free hand job, especially one provided by the masseuse at or towards the end of a massage." Now, I believe the latter definition—as crude as it may sound—solidifies the point I am trying to make here. *Really?* *Yes,* because that definition shows that uninvested, easy-breezy happy endings are attempts at replacing real love, vulnerability, and human experience. You see, wishing our story will have a complimentary conclusion void of great discoveries, challenges, and moments of growth is well, kind of like getting a free hand job when we could be making mad love that blows our minds and lifts our spirits. In the real, marvelous life you and I get to live right now, the obstacle is the path. Joy, fulfillment, self-expression, courage, love, and belonging only exist thanks to our ability to embrace our challenges and experience our feelings in the now.

Meet Christine.

In my early twenties, I lived in Nolita (in New York City) in a tiny third floor walkup on the corner of Prince Street and Mulberry. Christine worked a block away as the manager of a French boutique that sold the unusual combination of the two things that I love most on planet Earth—designer sunglasses and chocolate. I mean, *how dope is that?* Christine was funny, ambitious, kind, and incredibly fashionable. She was the kind of girl who wore things no one else could ever get away with, always looking fly in an effortless kind of way. However, hiding beneath her undeniable style and charming personality, Christine was terribly insecure about her body and always on the lookout for a new diet.

Christine's approach to food and exercise was as extreme as it gets—*all in* or *all out.* One moment she would be super exited to start a new diet and run six miles a day and the next she'd give up and walk next door to Lombardi's to order a large *margherita* with extra cheese. Each time she'd start anew, she'd buy into the illusion of a flawless future waiting for her, placing all her hopes for happiness, security, and even romantic love in the thin and sculpted body she would get one day soon. Essentially, she had created her own personal dream of living "happily ever after," and she wasn't going to stop until she got there.

"This is it!" she'd exclaim, while sipping on cayenne pepper and maple syrup lemonade—her lunch. "I just know this time is going to work. I have never felt more clear headed and filled with energy."

A week or two later, she'd walk into *Dean & Deluca* for a small treat, then meet some friends at a bar for a glass of wine, and suddenly the evening would turn into an excuse to indulge in way more food and alcohol than her body could possibly desire. Another diet failed, and with it, another dream collapsed. I watched her do this over and over and over again.

About a decade later, after a relocation to London and two career changes, Christine wrote me an email to let me know she would be in New York the following week and that we should meet for dinner at *Masseria dei Vini*, her favorite Italian restaurant in the city. Now a successful stylist with her own jewelry line and a popular column in a British fashion Magazine, Christine had every reason in the world to feel confident and proud of herself. And she was— proud of her career achievements, but hardly happy or confident.

Just like the old days, the night we got together, she ordered and ate more food than her body and mine combined could willingly consume. Like a train derailing at full speed, I watched the familiar agony take over.

"I shouldn't really eat this," she said taking a bite. "I am gluten intolerant. But I can't be in New York and not have pizza, right?" Half a slice later. "Can you believe how bloated I look? Seriously I look at list five months pregnant. I should buy something for colitis... Do you know of any good supplements?" Looking down at her empty plate. "I can't wait to have Tiramisu. I love the way they make it here." After her last bite. "Oh well... I may as well have another Prosecco. We are celebrating, right?"

I listened to her words pour out between bites, and, finally, when dessert cleared, she asked me what I'd been waiting for all night.

"How do you get to be even more fit now than ten years ago? You just had a baby for God's sake. Are you going to let me in on your secret?"

Christine was looking for the secret to magically transform her body, as if it was a pumpkin she could magically turn into a regal carriage.

"There is no secret Christine," I said. "There is no special meal plan to fix the way you feel right now, and there is no reason to keep punishing yourself either."

"What are you saying?" she asked, disappointed. "Did you become one of those people on a mission to convince the world women should just love being heavy, let themselves go, and embrace their fat body as it is?'

"No, not exactly. What I am saying, is that you need to start choosing *you*, and you have to start right *now*—in this moment. There is no such a thing as "a secret" or "a perfect day" to start honoring yourself, healing your wounds, and forming a true partnership with your body. All you have is today, imperfect as it may be, and you must make this moment right here a successful one."

"Today? How? Did you see what I just ate *for dinner*?"

"I did. And what I saw is yet more proof that your all or nothing approach to dieting doesn't work. Listen, I know for a fact that you called me because something in you is ready to get off the crazy weight rollercoaster that has consumed you since I have known you. You called me, because you are tired of putting yourself on hold, and for the first time in your life, you are willing to see things differently."

"I am happy to see you," Christine said with a smirk, "But you're right. I was hoping you'd tell me what to do to get rid of this damn weight once and for all."

"You choose yourself right *now*. That's what you do. You've got to stop using the imperfection of your present circumstances become an excuse to stop you from being fully present now, in this very moment. Own it fully. Acknowledge the guidance within you that made you reach out to me."

"So… give up on the dream to have a body I can feel proud of?"

"No, not unless you want to. Just give up on the illusion that you need to wait for a perfect moment to feel good enough. That is the only way it will ever come true."

CHOOSE NOW

Like Christine, you too are ready to choose *now*, to stop relating to those desires on a fantasy level, and to start dealing with them in the only reality we have available— *this very moment*. You see, unlike what the diet industry wants us to believe, it is not about the info, the plan, the ingredients, or the secret to getting what we so desperately desire. It all comes down to our ability to become present in the moment, so that we can access the guidance, the wisdom, and the self-worth that inherently belongs to us. When our choices come from a place of presence, our intention gets clear, our motivation gets strong, our actions align, and our body becomes our best ally.

This is not about renouncing to your desires or resigning yourself to your current shape and size, unless that is something you are totally cool with. There is no wrong desire. No wrong in wanting to look amazing, be successful, find a partner, get married, have a baby, move to Paris... or whatever else you truly want for yourself. I am *all* about wanting, having a vision, and *going for it!* However, we must keep in mind that although something or someone can make us happy for a certain period of time, inevitably after that, we will be faced with new challenges, and being happy will become, once again, a choice we make moment by moment.

If Cinderella (or pick your favorite Disney princess) was a real woman, like you and me, don't you think that at some point she would have struggled with weight gain, credit card debt, adult acne, infertility, miscarriage, postpartum depression, sickness of a loved one, betrayal, irritable bowel syndrome, anxiety disorder, diabetes, psoriasis, or at least a bad morning that lead to a domino effect of wrong decision making? Would you have loved her any less? Of course not. In fact, I am sure that if the story of Cinderella showed us a young girl who saved herself, learned her lessons, conquered her freedom, and then met her prince, we would have fallen madly in love with her and the combination of grace, flaws, wisdom, inner strength and resilience she stood for. I know, you may not see it now, but trust me, you are that girl. Stop putting her on hold.

FROM THEORY TO REALITY

If you have followed my instruction and completed the support work of the last chapter, then you have already taken the first important step to guide you out of the attic and toward your own path to freedom, without waiting for someone to hand over the keys— *You chose yourself.* And hopefully you are turning choosing you into a habit, knowing that each time you do so, you are creating an alliance between what you believe and what you desire, which is guiding you to start moving in a clear, powerful direction, closer and closer to the body you want, and the freedom you deserve. This second steps will allow you to continue on the journey. It will show you how to *disconnect* from the illusion of a perfect and unreal future self to connect with the real woman you are right now—one that creates her life one moment at the time instead of waiting for everything around her to be perfect enough to start living.

Now, I know this is far from the first time you heard about this concept of restoring our presence in *the now* and connecting to the present moment. But the power of *choosing now,* has little to do with mindfulness as a theory and everything to do with taking small consistent actions that will lead us closer and closer to freeing our body forever. In fact, let's move past the abstract and theoretical all together, to witness the effect of this second step, *choosing now*, by looking at two parallel scenarios in my friend Christine's reality. In both, she is the same body weight, working the same job, and living the same life.

Scenario # 1: The alarm goes off. Christine opens her eyes. As she rolls out of bed, the thoughts about last night pop into her mind, and almost instantly her solar plexus gets tight and her breath weakens. *I can't believe I finished that whole box of chocolate chip cookies before going to bed,* she thinks. *I have no discipline. I need to get serious about dieting or I'll die fat and lonely. Who would want to go out with someone this fat?* She grumbles, and heads down toward the bathroom, where she flips the light switch on. She squints her eyes open, and her reflection greets her in the mirror. Her skin looks dull—almost a greenish in tone. She stares at herself while brushing her teeth. *I look just like Mom,* she thinks to herself as she slathers on makeup over her unwashed face. *Fat, old, and tired.* Pulling her hair up and into a lazy, messy bun, she remembers that her fridge is packed with fresh veggies and organic eggs to make her favorite omelet for breakfast. But she feels too bloated to eat, so it's straight into her bedroom to put on the same black blouse and loose pants she wore yesterday. She takes a deep breath, grabs her purse, and walks out. As she locks the door behind her to go to her first meeting, she thinks to herself, *I would give anything to get back in bed, pull down the blinds, turn on TV, and call it a day.*

Scenario # 2: The alarm goes off. Christine opens her eyes. As she rolls out of bed, the thoughts about last night pop into her mind, and almost instantly her solar plexus gets tight and her breath weakens. *I can't believe I finished that whole box of...* She pauses for a moment, takes a deep breath, and says out loud. "I get it. It wasn't ideal, but I choose me, anyways." She sits on her bed for few more breaths, just enough time to notice the sunshine coming through her blinds, shining on the half-moon pendant her little sister bought her for her 30th birthday. She feels blessed to have Giulia in her life and decides to wear it every day this week to remind herself that she is never alone, and that it's okay to receive. She heads to the bathroom to get ready for her day, and as soon as she sees her image in the mirror... *I look kind of green...* the old judgmental thoughts quickly surface, but she says out loud, "I choose me! I am here." She washes her face, towels off, and smiles, realizing that her day hasn't even started, and she has already won—twice. After smoothing on shimmering eye shadow and a brush stroke of bronzer, she brushes her hair up into a sleek pony tail. *I'm really not hungry,* she thinks, so she puts on Meghan Trainor's playlist and whips up a veggie-omelet (so that she can have it later for lunch). Sipping her coffee, she gets dressed, and puts on the cozy *Alice and Olivia* cashmere poncho she just purchased at Bloomingdales. *Such a steal.* She touches the pendant, takes one last, deep breath to tune into to her Self before leaving her apartment. *It's Thursday! I can take Travis's yoga class after work.* She grabs her already packed gym bag and yoga mat, then walks out the door, eager to start her day.

Looking at the above scenarios, starring the same person, in the same situation, at the same body weight, in the same life, waking up after eating the same amount of cookies the night before, which version of Christine do you think has a better shot to free her body? Is it the woman who embraces the present moment no matter what happened yesterday, or the one who remains attached to what happened in the past, while placing all her hopes in something she will fix in the future? The only difference between the two is her willingness to choose herself and choose now.

I hate to be the kid in school who tells you that Santa doesn't exist, but I must say to you the same thing I said to

Christine. No doubt, that evening my words were not the smoothest or the easiest to receive, but I had known Christine for years, and I knew she was the kind of woman who, just like me, was all about real talk.

"If you start a diet or go on a fast tomorrow, you know exactly what will happen. It will work for a few days or maybe weeks, until you'll decide to have a glass of wine, a small bite of chocolate, or a tiny piece of bread. Within minutes, it will turn into a second glass of wine, a slice of pizza, a side order of French Fries, and then a bite of dessert, until you get back to your place for a pint of Haagen Das in bed. Because... *Oh well, you blew it today, may as well go for it!* The more you indulge, the more guilt you'll feel, and the more pressure you'll place on tomorrow, the day you will need to make up for your *eating mistakes*. Christine, this game, will never end unless you decide to end it —now."

She looked at me, holding her empty flute of Prosecco in her right hand, saying nothing for a long while.

"Is that what you did?" she asked, as she finally lowered the empty glass to the table. "End it?"

"Yes, that is exactly what I did. I stopped waiting for the perfect future, the fairytale that will never come, and chose to make my life what I want it to be, one moment at the time. I did that at time in my life, when I couldn't even move from my couch, when I thought I'd lost everything. Life only happens in the *now*. Happiness only exists in the *now*. And if you are not present *now, in your body*, because you are waiting for the day you'll be "good enough" to be rescued and live happily ever after, guess what? You are missing it."

Now was the one and only, albeit always available, shot that Christine had to shift her perception and move forward on the path to free her body. Trapped in Cinderella's attic, hostage to her compulsive thoughts about food, diets, needing to lose weight, and being unable to keep it off—what could Christine do in that moment, right there, sitting at the restaurant, overly full, and waiting for the check to come? She could say goodbye, order the express delivery of some kind of meal replacement plan, and start her next new diet tomorrow, hoping that this time she'd be diligent, impeccable and above all temptations, or she could *choose now* and move closer to what she most wanted— a life of joy, laughter, love, freedom, purpose, inspiration and true happiness.

Happiness, just like love, is an active state that is consciously created moment after moment, whether we are in the mood for it or not. It is something you must actively cultivate in order to possess. One day, we may have the money but not the time, the health but not the desire, the awesome partner but not a life purpose, or the great idea but not the resources to materialize it. Our job is *not* to keep our head down, sing a song, and suck it up until someone comes to save us or a fairy turns our worn-out Nikes and sweats into glass slippers and a dreamy gown. It's on us to be present to our lives, to discover our deepest desires, to stand up for ourselves, to show up deeply believing in our idea so that we can find the loving partner or the resources we need for our project or so they can find *us*.

It has almost been two years since that dinner in New York City, and Christine and I have worked together ever since. Today, she is in the best shape of her life, which is only one small aspect of a much greater victory. Knowing that she has the power to *choose herself,* and immediately elevate the way she feels about her life and her gorgeous body, is the real win. Today eating to satisfaction and exercising regularly are no longer sacrifices she needs to make or commitments she can break or fulfill, because they are nothing more than natural byproducts of the way she feels about her self—worthy, deserving, full, and willing to move one step after the other, without obsessing on what's missing or what should or could be different. She knows for certain that whenever Mr. Prince Charming will be ready to knock at her door, she'll welcome him and love him, because she *chooses* to and never because she needs him to save her, make her feel good enough, or complete her.

But now it's you I am trying to reach. Yes, you, the woman holding this book in your hands, at this very line, in this very paragraph of this second chapter. *In this moment.* Can you choose to find even one reason to elevate the way you feel about life and yourself. What can you do right now to rise above the pressure of feeling imperfect or dealing with less than ideal circumstances? Maybe you can bring your hands to your heart and take a few deep, clearing breaths, or maybe you can wear something that makes you feel good, pack your gym bag for tomorrow, go for a twenty-minute walk, or book a yoga class.

Or, are you thinking: *I can't choose myself right now? I really can't find even one reason to feel good in this moment about my life. This just doesn't work for me.* If you are, I hear you. I see you. I was you. I promise, I felt the same way, and I am by far the most skeptical person I know, so let my skepticism serve you, to ensure you that if I could do it—if I could *choose myself* and *choose the now*—so can you.

This is it, Woman. Your chance to stop looking for excuses to keep postponing your life, searching for that one fairytale moment: That one dance at the ball, that one diet that will make you thin enough to say *yes*, that one guy who will make you feel loved. It's on you. Listen to that little voice in the back of your head that whispers *there must be more to my life*, let it get louder, and *choose now*, without letting the inadequacy of your present circumstances stop you. *Choose now*, and every single moment will become an opportunity to move forward and create the changes you so desperately desire in your body and in your life. Write your own amazing story, one worthy of a powerful, imperfect, and unstoppable heroine, determined to show up for the challenge and choose herself, one moment at a time. Do not wait one more second.

Today, my 1980s original edition of Disney's *Cinderella* lives in my bookcase as a permanent reminder of how far I've come on this journey. I am not sure where my choices will lead me, or how exactly it will end, but I know for a fact that it will be one hell of an adventure.

Choose now and let your adventure begin.

SUPPORT WORK

POWER STATEMENT

*Write down the following power statement
and repeat it as often as you can.*

**"I choose now, and my ability to impact my life
and my body in this very moment."**

Repeat this statement to yourself or out loud whenever you experience a less than ideal moment during the day, so that you can strengthen the habit of placing who *You* are before what is happening to you or around you. In particular, observe the times you are future tripping, catching yourself eating something you don't approve of, or focusing on the gap between where you are and where you would like to be when it comes to your body, your life or your eating behavior. Right there, as you feel the sudden rise of frustration, anxiety, depression, and resentment towards your body or yourself, stop whatever it is you are doing, recognize the presence of an opportunity to choose, and repeat to yourself: **"I choose now,**

and my ability to impact my life and my body in this very moment." Then release any remaining guilt or shame so that you can start fresh without letting one unwanted action pull you straight back into the old loop.

YOUR FOUNDATION

Go back to page 48, copy down your Foundation Statement, then take five minutes to add to it any insights you have received from this chapter. Here are some examples: "I choose to believe this moment is all that I need to make the transformational change I desire," or "I choose to believe that I can create my own happy."

Remember, we don't want perfection. If your foundation statement feels good and believable to you when you repeat it out laud, you can trust that you are on the right path. Complete it now:

I choose to believe that I am

_____

_____

_____

Once you've written a statement that feels good to you, copy it down onto an index card, a piece of paper, or on your phone. Make sure you read it frequently, but at least once first thing in the morning, and once last thing at night.

TAKE ACTION

Continue to eat only when you are truly hungry, but add the following guideline each time you are having a meal:

Eat sitting down at a table and without engaging in any other activity.

I know this will be difficult for many of you, especially eating without distractions, but when our meals turn into a ritual to nurture and honor our self and our body, we change the intention and the energy behind our actions, which in turn impact our experience of pleasure, our sense of satiety, our appetite, and our digestive process as a whole. *It's not what we do, but why we do it and how we go about it. Remember?*

Change is happening now.

CHOOSE
TO TRUST

Florence has to be one of the most celebrated cities in the entire world. The architecture, the art, the food, the shopping, the wine. I mean, *who wouldn't love to live there, right?* That's what I kept telling myself, over and over again, after my husband and I made the inevitable decision to move our family back to Italy following his work relocation. July 4, 2016 was the day we said goodbye to our New York City apartment and boarded a one-way, direct flight to Rome. All I remember from that day is waiting for William to fall asleep, so that I could release the buildup of fear and anxiety that had preceded our move for weeks and allow tears to freely run down my cheeks.

"Come on Babe, it won't be forever," Alex reassured me. "Besides, you get to fly back as often as you like!"

But he had no clue. You see, for my husband, taking that flight back to Italy meant returning home after just four years living abroad. For me, it was going back to the crime scene, Trigger Town, the place where all my issues seemed to suddenly reappear in a matter of days. Unlike Alex, I had been living in the States for 19 years, and although I had visited the old country almost every summer, I had turned into a foreigner on vacation. In fact, I have become so American that on top of having a blue Passport, I now prefer Starbucks coffee over the creamy cappuccinos at the local *cafe*, can't live without gluten-free oatmeal for breakfast, demand my salad dressing on the side, and my scrambled eggs to be occasionally all white (which by the way, most Italians will consider somewhat of an insulting request). My professional life was also at a loss, for the fitness scene in the small city of Florence wasn't nearly as booming as it was in New York City or Los Angeles. There were no hip boutique fitness studios, no *Largree megaformer* machines, no *real* barre classes, and most importantly, no well-paid instructors.

"Maybe something great will come out of this. You are so resourceful! You will think of something."

This is what my analyst, Leah, kept telling me over our now *phone* sessions. She wasn't entirely wrong. It took me months, but eventually I decided to stop complaining to my husband, and everyone else I spoke to for more than 30 seconds, and face the fact that somehow, life had brought me back to Italy for a reason, one I didn't know yet, but one that I would sooner or later find out.

In the meantime, I had to do something with my time, so I started designing my own teaching method. I wanted to come up with a discipline that didn't require fancy equipment, something that merged my seasoned knowledge of high-intensity fitness with a more recent desire to find a deeper connection between mind, body and soul; A method I could teach no matter where I was living or traveling, and above all, one that built resilience—not just lean muscles.

The physical elements of my method were going to be easy to develop. Over the years, I had studied and collected over 15 certifications in all kinds of high-intensity fitness practices, which I could blend together in countless ways. Plus, I happened to have a real talent for encouraging women to push through a challenge, stay in it, and reach beyond their personal limits. The only thing missing was a way to include an introspective and spiritual element into my teachings, in a way that would elevate each movement into a powerful experience of connection. I gave myself a few months to research different styles of meditation, and whenever I could, I traveled the world to experience some of the most respected teachers and inspirational speakers, like Deepak Chopra and Eckhart Tolle.

That's how I found myself sitting at a Hay House event in London in early September 2017. It was 9:00 AM sharp when the oversized speaker-box beside me came to life, blasting Cold Play's "A Sky Full of Stars," and a petite blonde woman, dressed in distressed denim and nude pumps that matched her bodysuit, walked confidently to center stage. Almost instantaneously, hundreds of exultant Brits began dancing and waving their hands in the air. It was as if liquid adrenaline had been injected right into their veins, and suddenly I felt like I was at a rock concert.

Gabrielle Bernstein—the author of *The Universe Has Your Back*, a book that hooked me from the very first paragraph—didn't even speak. She danced, clapped, and eventually, with one hand holding the mic, raised the other to her heart. Right there, with just a nod of her head, she calmed, quieted, and seated the crowd.

At the time, all I knew about Gabby Bernstein came from that one book—her approach to prayer and meditation, her chosen sign of an owl to receive reassurance from the universe, and her longtime struggle with fertility and control issues. I sat impatiently through her long moment of silence, waiting to take notes in the brand-new Moleskin notebook opened on my lap, ready to get inspired by the way she led meditations, or possibly come up with the missing element for my teaching method.

"This is one of the happiest moments in my life…" Her voice cracked with the words, as her eyes filled with tears of joy. "And I am so psyched to be able to share it with all of you."

I'm having baby… those just had to be the next words, *I thought.* The ultimate proof that the Universe had her back all along and finally gave her what she most desired.

But oh, was I ever wrong. The joy she was sharing with the still-elated crowd was merely the experience of her newfound freedom—a freedom that came from surrendering her need to control life, all the while knowing *with absolute certainty* that her baby was on her way into her arms. *Okay,* I thought, knowing her book was about transforming fear into faith, about trusting that we are guided through a process that leads us back to love, about understanding that every obstacle is only a detour in the right direction… *so she isn't pregnant yet. Where is the proof?*

While other women jumped to their feet, I remained glued to my seat, unable to stand and partake in her "victory." *I* mean, *how was this even a victory?* In the world I lived in, you don't get a medal until you cross the line. There can be no celebration, joy, or reward until you get what you want—in Gabby's case, a positive pregnancy test. And yet, there she was, speaking with absolute conviction about something her own body had repeatedly failed to accomplish, something that no one could predict with certainty, and that no one could control. I have known plenty of women who have struggled with fertility issues, and never had I seen one vibrate with the same joy, as if she had heard her baby's heartbeat for the first time. Suddenly, as thoughts about conception, destiny, faith, and doubt began to jump into my head at an uncontrollable speed, I became aware of the familiar tight knot taking over the space normally occupied by my solar plexus. I knew this clenching feeling. I was triggered, and there was only one thing I could do.

I chose myself in that moment, the me that existed beyond my reaction and the doubts in my mind, and the me who knew that freedom was always one choice away.

Within seconds, I stopped listening to Gabby and began to breathe as smoothly as I could, grounding my feet with intention and consciously expanding my ribcage a little more with each inhale. In due time, I looked up to her again, standing proud in her pumps and pausing every so often to feel her audience, and I allowed myself to connect with her presence and receive her message with ease and clarity—penetrating my own resistance. She might not have a baby in her womb, and her words might have been too audacious for me at that time, but I could feel her already vibrating as the woman she wanted to be—*a mother*. That was as undeniable as her confidence, which was exposing my own fear of taking a leap of faith and standing up for what I most desired.

Gabby wanted to be a mother. I wanted to be an inspirational speaker and author who empowers women to free themselves from food and body obsession. Yet I was afraid to express that desire out loud, or even entertain the idea of pursuing it fully. I kept my dream to myself, shrinking it, trying to make it more reasonable or logically obtainable, believing that I couldn't possibly aspire to more than being a successful fitness professional. How could I? I needed proof, some evidence that I was made for bigger and better things. A book deal? An invite from Dr. Oz? Just something tangible that would allow me to believe I had a shot, something other than the whispering voice in my heart begging me to show up for it. I didn't trust the process. In fact, I didn't even truly understand what that meant. Yet that woman on stage did, and the example she was setting for me needed no explanation. From that moment on, I forgot about my meditation research, as I realized there was a bigger question I needed to answer: Could I *say Yes* to myself, my body, and my burning desire to serve other women in a big way before having 100% of the details figured out and holding in my hands evidence that I too was worthy of all that I desired?

What we are waiting for is not as important
as what happens to us while we are waiting.
Trust the process.
—Mandy Hale

THE PROCESS

The word 'process' comes from Old French *process,* which means 'a journey,' and from the Latin *processus,* "a going forward, advance, progress." However, as evidenced by Merriam-Webster, modern times have skewed the definition to *process,* "a natural phenomenon marked by gradual changes that leads toward a particular result."

The notion of "following a process" is widely accepted and scrupulously applied to almost every area of our lives. There is a process and a plan for everything: degree-earning, sport-training, business-coaching, meal-cooking, movie-making, child-birthing, book-writing, social-researching, partner-matching, bridge-building, and whatever-doing. We have since made "following the process" a phrase interchangeable with "following a prescribed protocol to produce a desired result." Yet, when it comes to the realms of psychology, spirituality, and self-development, a process cannot be limited to a specific path for growth, that everyone can indiscriminately follow to a measurable outcome. Instead, we find ourselves returning to the Old French meaning, which is something more along the lines of an individual journey to discover our emotions, understand our inner world, and remove the blocks that keep us from being connected with our truth.

Wait! you may be thinking *I thought this book was about freeing our body, finding ease around food and getting in the best shape of our lives. Why are we talking about trusting the process, feeling supported, and having faith in something greater than us?* Well, learning to trust that there is a process for each and every one of us—an individual journey of self-discovery to embark upon, one that can't be compared to anyone else's—may be the most important conversation we need to have when working on healing food obsession and negative body image issues.

Whether you generally struggle with the way you look, or you identify as a food addict, an overeater, a person suffering from bulimia, anorexia, or body dysmorphia, the ability to diet, regulate food, and monitor body weight, offers a small sphere of control in a world that is scary and uncontrollable, and it is essential that we recognize that. Think about it, no matter what happens in our lives or how scared we are about the future, we can always project all our worries into one singular element of our lives we need to manage, like our body weight, for example. Chances are that food or abstention from it (whichever way you choose to look at it), has become an integral part of the way you attempt to quiet the chaos within, and thus cope with your fear. Once fear takes over, the actions you take and decisions you make are driven by the need to control.

Meet Nora.

Nora was born with the ability to rapidly envision the most efficient way through any task, activity, project, problem, or challenge. This made her tremendously useful to many people—especially to her boss, and to the nonprofit organization where she sat as the head of the Board of Directors for over twelve years. However, the same qualities that made her valuable to some, made her resentful to others.

Terrible at delegating, Nora expected everyone to think and act just like her, for she knew the best and the fastest way to get the job done right. Her relationship to food was a perfect mirror of her control issues. Behind closed doors, she was a professional dieter, whom after years of Weight Watchers, believed the only way to keep her weight down was by replacing two meals a day with protein shakes—*for the rest of her life.* Her inner condition reflected the efficient yet anxious way she ate, which was often standing in her kitchen gulping down her protein drink while checking multiple emails or returning phone calls. Same with exercise, which was nothing more than an outlet to practice discipline on herself and dominate her body.

On the rare occasions that Nora attended my classes, there was always something she felt compelled to ask me to fix. The room was too cold or too hot, the music too loud, or the class too crowded. She preferred one on one sessions, and even then, I could sense she had a hard time letting herself be guided. I knew that if I wanted to help her, she needed to increase body-awareness and disconnect from the underlying fear and anxiety that lived beneath her need for control. I also knew it wasn't going to be easy. For months, I focused all of our sessions exclusively on practicing grounding, tracking breath, and finding a sense of center through intense conscious movement. At times, I could feel her energy shift into a more receptive, softer, and loving presence, but even then, I had a feeling she wasn't able to take that connection out of the studio and into her daily life.

Before working together, Nora and I had known each other socially for years and I was familiar with the baseline of her *home-story,* which went something like, *"Unless I am perfect, I will be left behind."* The middle child of three girls, Nora grew up feeling lonely and unloved. Her mother always favored her older sister, while her father had a soft spot for the baby of the family. Besides her dad, Nora had loved two other men and eventually, they both left her for someone else—a younger, thinner, and less controlling woman. She was convinced that, *"If I was thin and pretty enough, none of that would have ever happened."*

By the time Nora turned forty-six, the pressure of living by her harsh sets of reference points had built so much resentment within her, that although she was still young, she decided to step down from her role as the board director and find something else to focus on in her life. Yet, even in the midst of the very action of resigning, she was determined to retain some kind of control. After writing the most beautiful resignation letter, Nora called in a meeting with the entire board to read it out loud and announce her decision. With perfect diction and impeccable delivery, she dove deep into her feelings and shared how much that community had meant to her over the years. Coming to the end of her letter, with her eyes still down to the page, she rejoiced in the anticipation of delight for how disappointed and upset every single person would certainly be about her choice, but when she looked up to the room, there were no epic reactions and no objections—not a single one. On the contrary, the board members appeared to be unanimously relieved. Within days, a new young woman stepped into her role, and although she wasn't nearly as efficient or as well prepared for the position, she was up for the challenge and willing to learn.

Understandably, Nora felt wounded, betrayed, and abandoned. She had devoted all of her time and effort to that organization for so many years, and no one, not a single person, had given her the recognition she expected and desired. Once again, life proved to her that she was destined to be replaced by someone else, someone thinner, younger, and more lovable than she could ever be.

When I saw Nora about a week after the resignation fiasco went down, I knew she had hit rock bottom and there could only be one way left to go—up. I didn't like to see her suffer, but I was positive that her difficult experience was a great opportunity for her to break her patterns and find herself. The woman standing behind that need to control was kind, brilliant, and incredibly resourceful, and finally Nora could have the opportunity to meet her. All that was required was her willingness to recognize that beneath all the apparently valid reasons she had to keep feeling neglected and abandoned, there was a life-changing lesson waiting to be uncovered.

TRUST IS THE ONLY WAY

If we do not trust the process, we cannot experience freedom, and without freedom, no results will ever last or mean anything. Any time we start something, there's a process to its realization—not a plan. In fact, unlike what we like to believe, our lives rarely shift in orderly, clear, linear 1-2-3 step programs.

As scary as that is, the moment we let go of the illusion of control and lean into the uncertainty, we *choose to trust*, and everything shifts for the better—*as it did for me.*

A few months after returning from London, I flew to Los Angeles with my family for a 3-week vacation. The first thing I did (well, after driving to Starbucks at 5:00 AM sharp and ordering a Grande Almost Misto with Blonde Roast) was drive to Pilate Plus for Lacey's Megaformer class. Still holding onto my Starbucks' cup, overjoyed by the idea of finally sipping on hot coffee in a portable device, I walked into the studio, hugged my friend, and chose a machine next to a beautiful woman who was about my age.

"I love your leggings," she said as soon as I settled in. "Where did you get them?"

"Carbon 38. I have a discount code if you like. I can give it to you after class."

"Oh, that's so nice. Thank you. Are you a fitness instructor?"

"Yes, I am."

"What do you teach?"

"Well... At the moment I am working on my own mind and body method. It's a high intensity mind and body approach to build resilience."

"Oh my god! We should talk! I am a clinical psychologist and I've been teaching resilience training for 15 years. I'd love to find out what your method is all about…"

I believe that Dr. Alexa Altman was not early for a 5:45 AM class, nor sitting on a machine right next to me, nor liking my two-year-old *Michi* leggings by coincidence. Alexa's knowledge and insights helped me to turn my method into a cutting-edge mind and body approach to resilience training, which is now known as Fuel: The Body Resilience Training. I didn't realize that right away, but it turns out I had created a discipline that was the perfect mirror of what it means to trust the process. An outlet to use life's obstacles with intention, lean into the uncertainty, and turn unpleasant feelings into fuel to ignite inner-fire and bring forth transformational change in people's bodies and lives.

The day of the very first Fuel class, I hung a large poster that read in bold letters *"All feelings allowed"* outside of the studio to remind everyone, including myself, that although calories would be burned and muscles would be toned, our true intention would always be moving and touching something that lived deep beneath our skin. Loneliness, sadness, fear, anxiety, could all be felt and transmuted into powerful energy and moved through physical activity, the same way the waste-to-energy process generates electricity and heat to illuminate entire cities, directly through waste combustion.

People were moved by what was happening in the safe space I was holding for them and by the miracles they started to witness in their lives. Suddenly, weight was melting off people's bodies, retired athletes were competing again, single mothers were opening new businesses, and those who had been longtime singles were dating and starting new relationships. Generally speaking, everyone, including myself, felt and looked younger, happier, softer, sexier, more present, and more focused on what really matters. All this, I believe, was possible because little by little, we each began to trust the process and release our need to control what wasn't going according to plan—*our plan* that is.

BELIEVE BEFORE YOU SEE

It was the last day of the year, and I was hosting my first Fuel workshop in New York City called *Final Let Go*. At that point, I hadn't taught in New York in over a year, and I was nervous as hell. I had sent out an invitation to old clients, mentors, colleagues, and friends, inviting them all to attend a unique movement experience designed to release their mind and body from negative emotions and judgments accumulated over the course of the previous twelve months. None of them had ever experienced my new teaching style, and for the most part, they didn't even suspect I had any interest in the subjects of spirituality or self-development.

That morning I arrived early, as I always do, ready to set up the room, check the sound system, light the candles, burn the incense, and tune in with myself to prepare to serve my class, uncertain who would be showing up. Outside the door, sitting on the staircase waiting, I saw Nora. I hadn't seen her in over a year and she looked…well, different. I gave her a long hug, then told her I'd love to catch up for coffee after class.

This is the perfect workshop for her. I thought to myself as I walked into the room, and the fact that she had showed up, without first sending me a long list of questions to find out in detail what this movement experience was going to be all about, told me she was finally ready to release her need to control. When I opened the door for everyone to come in, Nora took a seat on a mat all the way in the back of the room. Not long after that, a whole crowd of familiar faces showed up. Among them, I noticed a new woman coming through the door, a friend of a friend. She was a tall, thin, 30-something with long, straight, chestnut hair falling over a vintage

Madonna shirt that was at least two sizes too big for her body. I walked my way through the mats to welcome her and invite her to find a seat on whichever spot remained available. She looked around the room to locate an empty mat and her dark eyes suddenly widened.

"Is that Nora?" she whispered.

"Yes. Do you know her?"

She nodded.

I was ready to ask for details or maybe walk her to Nora, but the room was packed, and it was time to start. So, I excused myself, moved to the front of the room and announced to everyone to please stand on their mat, ground their feet, and take a moment to arrive—the whole of them, body, feelings, reactions, fears and frustration.

"We are here to observe ourselves. That's all. Remember, all feelings and no judgments. Not even judgments about your judgments. We all have them." Then I turned to my phone, selected the playlist, and *Step Out* by Jose Gonzales and The Chainsmokers filled the room.

After a walking meditation, I asked each participant to find a spot on the wall, turn to face the center of the room, and meet me in a ninety-degree wall squat. They would hold this position for 4 minutes in total with the intention to connect to the discomfort rather than escape it. Two minutes in, I asked them to envision a center line running through the middle of their body and witness what needs to happen to find an alignment between the way they felt about themselves, how they wished they could feel, what they wanted for the new year, and what they were willing to release from the one coming to an end. During the last minute, I invited everyone to reach their hands out and firmly hold onto one another, while maintaining the increasingly uncomfortable position. Here, they fully experienced what it means to feel supported, while at the same time to intentionally sustain those around us.

"Anyone want to share anything before we move on?" I asked as they slid down the wall after the exercise was over.

"I just want to say thank you," said Claire, the new girl. "I can't even begin to tell you how strange and... well, perfect this exercise was today. I know it was only a few minutes, but in those few minutes I understood something I never did before. It just clicked for me."

She paused for a few breaths as a tear spilled down her cheek.

"No matter what I do, or how hard I try, I always feel *this pressure* of never being as great as other women around me, starting with my own mom and my older sister. It's like I am always a step behind them. I've never been as popular, as smart, or as beautiful. I never got into Harvard and I didn't make Partner in our family's firm before turning thirty. And it's not just my family. It's everywhere. Of all the men in New York City, I fell in love with a widower, and no matter how much I love him… and I do…there is this doubt, this *feeling*, that I will never be as close to him as his first wife."

She paused again, as the woman sitting next to her reached for the box of tissue I had placed by her side.

"Here you go, love."

Claire wiped her tears away, then spoke again.

"Thank you. Really…I feel so much love from all of you… Even from you."

Claire was now looking straight at Nora. I took a quick pick around the room, wondering if I should interrupt her, or somehow moderate the exchange between the two women.

"When the board asked me to step in," Claire continued, "I accepted. That is what I always do, step into the place of an incredible woman like you, so that I can be reminded of how unprepared I am. All I heard this year was, *'Nora used to do it this way,' 'Nora took care of all this,' 'Nora had no problem doing that in time.'* I resented you so much Nora, but I get it. It has never been about you… I am so sorry… I really am."

98

As the younger, thinner, more lovable woman who took her place kept speaking, Nora remained silent, but I noticed she had a soft look on her face that she had never worn before.

"And just now" Claire went on, " in the exercise we just did, I trusted in my own feet, my own back, my own breath, while at the same time, for some strange reason, I felt supported and close… to you"

Nora walked over to Claire, hugged her tightly, long enough for their bodies to melt into one another, as the rest of us sat there, holding space for the very special moment that brought evidence that the Universe works in divine ways.

"This whole year or more has been…" Nora said, "I don't know, difficult, enlightening, painful, strangely awesome, and… definitely confusing. I left the Board because I was desperate to feel wanted and important, and then I watched you all move on so easily without me. All those years trying to control *every little thing*… turn each challenge into a success… for what?"

She smiled, paused, then spoke again.

"For nothing. That's exactly for what. Nothing. And now I have nothing to do, nothing to manage or fix, and nothing to control, and you know what's funny?" Nora looked straight at me. "For some strange reason, I am okay with that."

There it was, the full circle of how the process works its magic, and how miracles happen in the most amazing and un-expected ways. For Nora, Claire was the new, young girl who stole her light, and for Claire, Nora was the worthier woman who made her feel insecure. Both were victims of a story, both suffered, and now both had an opportunity to trust the process and find their individual paths to healing. The moment Nora chose to trust, a great wide expanse of fearlessness opened up before her. Not because she suddenly experienced no fear, but rather because she *chose herself* and acted despite her fear. In other words, she chose to fear less.

That boldness, and faith is exactly what triggered me back in London. Gabby proudly standing on stage in front of hun-dreds other women, vibrating with the certainty of her future motherhood, didn't come with absence of fear, but with major courage. So please, as you prepare yourself to take this step, don't ever think for a moment that surrendering or trusting the process means saying, *"Oh well… I'll just sit, pray, focus on positive thinking and watch my life happen,"* or, *"Ok, I'll channel my thoughts into the image of Gisele Bundchen's body so that my ass could mold into hers while it rests on the meditation pillow."* Sorry, but you still have to go for it, be vulnerable, take risks, get out there in a big way, and work your ass off when needed. What must change is your energy and the intention behind all you do.

Choosing to trust the process allows you to know for certain that no matter what happens, you are in the right place for that moment, even if in that very moment you can't possibly understand why. You are there to see and learn something you absolutely need, and that no matter what, you are worthy of your desires, and you are never alone.

On July 12, 2018, I was in sitting on my meditation pillow. As I focused on my breath and began to tune inward, I felt called to pick up my phone and check my Instagram feed. I tried to resist it at first, but finally I gave in, and the moment I clicked on the IG icon, there she was, almost one year since that Hay House event, Gabby Bernstein sporting an adorable baby bump announcing to the world what she had known all along—she was becoming a mother.

She believed before she could see, and now the whole world could see with her. Sunshine flooded my soul. Never had I been happier for someone I barely knew. It wasn't just joy for a new baby coming into the world or for an incredible woman finally getting what she most wanted, but it was the sparkle of hope and faith I needed to keep choosing myself, trusting that my desires would be met—knowing that true alignment could be created, when you are brave enough to lean into the unknown and choose to trust. Suddenly, everything made sense. I could see, without a doubt, that I had to move back to Italy, feel disoriented with nothing to teach and no one to teach it to, all in order to experience that fear of uncertainty in the depth of my being, and understand that it could become fuel for something incredible. In other words, I had to lose my entire safety net to realize what existed beyond it.

The unshakable awareness that we are always support-ed, allows us to navigate the obstacles in our lives and remain committed to our freedom along the way. So, whatever your desires are, including those of getting your body into the best shape of your life and freeing yourself from food and body image obsession, know in your heart that mind blowing results are on the way, with absolute certainty. Remember that the path to happiness and fulfillment is not a path for the few, as so often we are led to believe, but a path that everyone can sus-tain as long as they are willing to choose themselves, tune into the moment, trust the process, and take one step at the time. Need one more proof? I once dreamed of being an author, and I was so convinced I t wasn't possible for me I kept that desire to myself for decades, and now, here you are, reading my first book.

You see, as I told you from the very first line, I am abso-lutely certain you were guided to pick up this book and the fact that you are still readying it, means that you are ready. Ready to reclaim your freedom. Ready to let go of a life time of false projections and limiting beliefs. Ready to free your body and show up fully into your life. Ready to recognize that you are always guided.

Whether you can fully see it or not, there is a powerful force for good within you and around you. You can call it the Universe, Mother Nature, Divine Intelligence, God, or anything you please. That presence of infinite wisdom is always there to help you find alignment, rise above temporary circumstances, connect with your truth, and trust that your heartfelt desires are meant to come to life. All it takes is your willingness to take one step after the other. So here comes your next step, choose to trust. Take a deep breath in and step fully into it knowing in your heart that your best body and life already awaits you.

SUPPORT WORK

POWER STATEMENT

*Write down the following power statement
and repeat it as often as you can.*

"I choose to trust that I am always supported."

Use this statement whenever you feel lost, alone, afraid, and doubtful about being able to feel free and confident in your own body. Those fearful moments are opportunities to choose to restore your faith in the Universe. As soon as you notice your doubts about this work, and begin too ques-tion your process, know it is a normal part of the journey. In fact, I want you to expect doubts, and be prepared for them, especially as we get deeper in the work. So as soon as you notice the pres-ence of doubt or fear, acknowledge the thought and go straight into your power statement: **"I choose to trust that I am always supported."**

YOUR FOUNDATION

Go back to page 74, copy down your Foundation Statement, then take five minutes to add to it any insights you have received from this chapter. Here are some examples: "I choose to believe there is a bigger and better plan, one where I get to be free and look amazing", or "I choose to believe I am supported, and I have been guided into this life changing path to freedom and ease.". Let this exer-cise come easily, and trust that if your foundation statement feels good and believable to you, you are good to go. Complete it now:

I choose to believe that I am

_____

_____

_____

Once you've written a statement that feels good to you, copy it down onto an index card, a piece of paper, or on your phone. Make sure you read it frequently, but at least once first thing in the morning, and once last thing at night.

TAKE ACTION

Continue to eat only if you are truly hungry, sitting down at a table and while not engaging in other activities, but add the following guideline each time you are having a meal:

Taste and enjoy your food fully, placing the fork on the table after each mouth full to focus on chewing and savoring what you are eating.

When we give ourselves permission to savor each bite, noticing the textures, spices, and sensations on our palate, we communicate a sense of safety and ease to our body, and we gradually release the illusion of not having enough so that we stop holding on tightly to what doesn't serve us, body weight included. Remember, you don't have to be perfect in your practice, you just have to show up consistently and remain willing to choose yourself one moment at the time.

Change is part of a bigger and better plan.

CHOOSE
TO FORGIVE

When I finally moved into my first house (a small, mid-century fixer-upper overlooking the Hollywood hills, which needed far more work than I could have ever imagined) my very first project was turning the dry, outdoor-space into a garden worthy of the cover of *Garden Design Magazine*. With that in mind, and zero experience in landscaping, I took a trip to Hollywood Home Depot, bought a plum tree and a bunch of colorful plants, stuck them in the ground arranged by color scheme, poured some water on their leaves, and then stretched out on my deck exhausted, sunburned, and eager to witness my dream garden grow before my eyes in the weeks to come. Now, I must say I got lucky with the flowers. Apparently, pansies and nasturtiums don't need an experienced gardener to look pretty and survive for a few months, but the large and gorgeous plum tree that cost me a small fortune, was looking sickly.

Weeks had gone by and I had watered it plenty, without missing a day. *Why wasn't it blooming?* My neighbor Ed had four healthy fruit trees, all thriving, less than twenty yards away, so it couldn't have possibly been the dry weather. It had to be something I was doing…

"My plum tree is dying," I said, catching Ed pulling into his driveway one evening after work. "Go ahead, tell me, please. What am I doing wrong?"

"You are doing nothing wrong," he said, with a kid-like grin on his face. "Except, you have planted your tree in an unforgiving soil."

"An unforgiving soil?" I repeated after him. "What does that even mean?"

Ed went on to explain all the options I had available to turn my dry rocky soil into soft and fertile ground, but all I could think about was the word *unforgiving*, now playing on repeat in my head. That, and the fact that I had failed at yet another project.

Planting a plum tree into a hard and impenetrable soil, could now be added to my lengthy list of shortsighted decisions. There I was, twenty-six years old, working relentlessly to avoid acknowledging that I had wasted four years of my life, and thousands of dollars, building a recording studio in Los Angeles that was both a terrible idea and a big-time flop. To top that, I had taken a half-ass attempt at becoming a recording artist, which also turned out to be an embarrassing fiasco.

The evidence of defeat was all around me, but I was unwilling to accept it, and above all, I was unwilling to let go of my desire to prove that my parents were wrong about me. To them I had never been thin enough, graceful enough, smart enough, successful enough, it-doesn't-matter-what *enough*, and I was desperate for retribution. One way or another, I would show them what I was capable of and they would have to admit to it. So, instead of cutting my losses and moving on with my life, I kept going, month after month, investing more time, and more money, hoping to make it work, all while digging a deep dark hole for myself and my finances.

Resentment fueled my every move, and persisted despite fatigue and disappointments. Every single day, I'd wake up at four o'clock in the morning to abuse my body with a heavy workout session, followed by a fort-five-minute run. Then, I'd spend the next fourteen hours or so juggling between a demanding full-time day job, and the stressful chase for broke musicians, flaky producers, and wannabe rock stars, all of which comes with owning and managing a Hollywood studio. There was no joy in my life, no connection with myself, no feeling of trust or surrender, just a whole lot of pressure, anxiety, and force. And the craziest thing about all of it, is if it wasn't for my own body's intervention, I could have kept going that way *for years*.

The day I took a shower and saw with horror that I was losing hands-full of hair, I knew in an instant, I had gone too far. The truth, in that very moment, became clear as day. Sooner or later, *what I was doing to myself, was going to kill me.*

The process of closing my business and leaving the music studio I had built from scratch wasn't nearly as difficult as facing how I felt about the whole thing. I decided to escape. I'd leave town, without a plan, to avoid seeing the closed storefront, avoid friends asking me how I was doing, and most of all, avoid calls from my parents telling me, "If only you had listened to us, you could have saved yourself thousands of dollars and years of your life." Mostly, I wanted to avoid myself, the extra fifteen pounds I had put on in just two weeks, and the deep, rotten knot in my stomach that kept me constipated and looking at least four months pregnant. So, I packed all my shame and resentment with a few travel essentials; passport, headphones, sleeping pills, sweatshirts, sneakers, Tums, my journal…then took a taxi straight to LAX.

Nothing on earth consumes a man more quickly
than the passion of resentment.
—Friedrick Nietzsche

LET THE WEIGHT GO

According to Merriam-Webster, resentment is "a feeling of indignant displeasure or persistent ill will at something regard-ed as a wrong, insult, or injury." The word resentment comes from the Latin word *sentire* which means 'to feel' and the use of 're' in front of any word, means 'again.' Therefore, "resent-ment" literally means 'to feel again.' In fact, when we don't forgive, we are destined to feel something we didn't want to feel in the first place, again and again and again. That indig-nation or ill will becomes a focal point in our lives that keeps us hooked in the past and unable to commit fully to the pres-ent. Although it causes us pain, we stay attached to it and we feed the connection with the very experience or person who hurt us, making it stronger one thought at a time. But that's not all. Holding onto resentment is one of the most insidious reasons for emotional eating and self-sabotage. In fact, unless we address the anger and grief we carry from our past, we'll have no other choice but to plant the seeds of our desires in a body engrossed in bitterness, hardened by pain, and unavail-able to restore the self-regulating ability we were all born with. Until we choose to forgive, we can't free our body.

Santorini in May was chilly, beautiful, and free from the invasion of tourists, who gather in flocks on the coast of the island to capture the stunning sunsets of all shades blue and white from June to September. The small hotel where I stayed was almost all mine, with the exception of an older couple visiting from Southern Italy. The first day I got there, I slept for 13-hours straight, and woke up to an earnest desire to go outside and move my body, wanting to breathe, to expand, and to connect to that undefined part of myself that existed beyond my name, my age, my professions, and above all, my recent mistakes. Every day, I woke up at dawn, and ran to an old Seal playlist, which had out of the blue, popped-up on my iTunes. Inevitably, by the time I would get to the second instrumental of the final song, 'Don't Cry', a hurricane of emotions would take over my body like a vortex, pulling me in and through until I stopped moving. I'd sit on the ground and bring both hands to my heart as it bounced aggressively off my chest. And about ninety seconds into it, the pain would turn into relief. The tension, self-denial, and pressure that I held inside like a secret no one should keep, would move out of my body though my sweat and tears. Each morning, right there, in the midst of that intensity, I'd feel a new and undefined sense of presence and connection, an experience of freedom that I can only describe as being imperfectly and miraculously—*human*.

During my escape in Greece, I got to know the only other guests in my hotel, Anita and Joe, who were celebrating their fiftieth wedding anniversary. Often in the evening, the three of us would sit together on our tiny hotel terrace, overlooking the unique site of tropical and volcanic landscape, while sharing a bottle of local wine and talking about all sorts of interesting things: Sicilian food, baroque art, love, family, and faith. My parents had been together for decades, but I had yet to see, with my own eyes, an older couple being still so much in love. Joe was an entertaining man, the kind who could talk about his life for hours without asking you a single question, yet still make you feel part of a conversation. But it was something that Anita said to me which moved me the most.

"It's so peaceful out here," Anita said as soon as she saw me coming down the stairs ready for my Seal-soaked run, one early morning. She was sitting on the porch all by herself, wrapped up in a large blanket, and sipping on mint tea.

"Yes, it's beautiful," I said. "But it's also very cold. Do you need anything?"

"No dear…but… there is something I want to tell you."

"To me? Of course!"

I zipped up my jacket, then I obediently took a chair from a distant table and pulled it next to her. Anita kept her eyes at a distance, immersed in the wildflower-dotted landscape that covered much of the hill on the horizon.

"Life wasn't always easy with Joe." She took a long pause, as if her mind turned back in time to remember what happened one last time. "He broke my heart once, and it was so terribly painful. I thought I'd never breathe fully again."

"I am sorry, Anita. I—"

"—I couldn't believe the man I loved so much, with whom I had three children, could do something so terrible to me, but he did. He had an affair with one of my dearest friends. I never wanted to see him, or her, again. That was forty years ago." She paused, then she looked at me and smiled with the warmth and motherly kindness a mature woman is sometimes able to share with a young girl. "You weren't even born yet."

"I am *so* sorry. That must have been so painful… but I can see you've worked things out. You look at him with so much love now…"

"No dear, the man you see me looking at today is not the boy I met when I was only thirteen years old, not even the man I married. My relationship with him ended a long time ago—after he broke my heart. The man you see by my side is the man I had to meet, know, and fall in love with all over again. And this time around, love wasn't at first sight. Loving him was a choice, one I still make every single day."

I was not sure why Anita shared that story with me. Maybe she saw my heart melting at the site of such a cute, loving couple, and felt the need to acknowledge that it wasn't always so easy. Nonetheless, I felt grateful for the fresh prospective on what forgiveness could be like. Anita forgiving her husband for a painful infidelity did not mean reconciling with the idea of the man she knew before, but rather giving him the opportunity to sweep her off her feet as a brand-new man, one she could meet and learn to love, maybe even more than the one she met a lifetime ago.

I wanted that for myself. To see *me* detached from my own mistakes. I couldn't turn back time, magically refill my bank account, or repair the broken pieces of my life, to return it to what it was before I lived it, but I could make it something new, unique, wonderful, and abundant. I wanted to be someone I met for the first time on that coast, someone who showed up with open arms and an open heart, rather than an oversized backpack full of failures, resentment, and disappointments. I had to find a way to release all of that, once and for all.

On my last day on the island, I purchased the most gorgeous set of parchment papers, sat alone on the small balcony of my hotel room overlooking the ocean, and wrote a heartfelt forgiveness letter to my mom and dad. I witnessed my feelings pour out of me and effortlessly drop onto the page. One word after another, I honored each painful experience and declared it time to *choose me*, to let go of what happened, release my parents' opinions, and clear myself from their judgment. It belonged to them, not to me. What they said and what they did to me would never be right, and there would be no apologies or recognition, at least not in the way I had fantasized up until that day, but I was no longer willing to punish myself for it. Not even one moment longer. When it felt complete, I read the letter aloud, undisturbed by the fact that my parents would never get to read it, or understand what it meant to me. My forgiveness was not about them after all. It had become all about freeing *me* and giving myself a chance to live a life moved by the desires in my heart, rather than my thirst for retaliation. Once I got to the end, I placed the six-page letter in a porcelain bowl, set in on fire, and watched the paper turn to ashes before my eyes. It's hard to put into words the healing I experienced in that moment, but there is something I do remember with unquestionable clarity. The next morning, as I left the island, my heartburn was gone, my skin looked exceptionally refreshed, and my clothes felt a little loose on me.

Meet Rebecca.

It took six months before I noticed a change in Rebecca's attitude. It all started with something that had nothing to do with her body — a painful breakup with her boyfriend of six years. I didn't know the details, but her heartache and rage for what Ben did to her could be felt from across the room. Her stress levels had increased, to the point where I could detect an actual change in her endurance and flexibility. It was as though she was inhabiting the body of a much older and stiffer woman, instead of the vibrant one I had worked with for over two years. Week after week, our sessions began to turn into a task Rebecca felt the need to complete, rather than what they used to be—an opportunity to connect to her body and walk out feeling unstoppable. The impact that resentment was having on Rebecca, didn't stop with her workouts. Her mental and emotional state directly triggered a cycle of emotional eating and self-loathing she so desperately wanted to free herself from, and before she knew it, she had hooked back into the vicious loop of sadness, stress, craving, shame, and punishment that she had walked away from almost two years before.

This is what it looked like:

Each time Rebecca thought about her ex-boyfriend, she experienced an overwhelming mixture of sadness, rage, discouragement, and anxiety.

The stress level in her body increased, the knot in her stomach tightened, her breath weakened, and her entire body contracted. Even her posture changed by slightly shifting her shoulders forward, as if she was attempting to secure the raw wounds in her broken heart.

To anesthetize from the pain and discomfort, her brain activated Rebecca's go-to defense mechanism to repress all unpleasant emotions: Cue emotional eating.

A whole bag of chips and a pint of ice-cream later, after a very brief moment of numbness, she would finally remember that no amount of goodies would ever be enough to feed what she was truly craving— *love, connection, and reunion with the one she had lost.*

In the face of her stuffed and bloated belly, Rebecca would feel even more resentful towards her ex-boyfriend and towards herself. You see, no matter how angry she was towards him, deep down she believed that if she was thinner, sexier, smarter, or more in control of her emotions, he would still be with her and none of that would have happened in the first place.

But the damage of the cycle didn't end there. Combine the original resentment she felt from being dumped, with the newly built-up bitterness and shame she experienced for over-eating, and before you know it, her stress level would be even higher than it originally was. In other words, if the pain, hurt, and rage of her break up was already high to start with, by the time Rebecca stuffed herself with food, her stress level would go through the roof.

Then what?

Rebecca would go straight back into her usual cycle and hit the kitchen again. *Resentment → stress → eat → shame → resentment → stress → eat → shame*— the vicious loop she was destined to repeat, *indefinitely*, until she could come to terms with what was happening in her life and make the only choice that could permanently change everything—*choosing herself,* right now, and trusting that despite feeling hurt and abandoned, she could still be free. To get there, she had to choose to forgive.

"What do you feel when you witness yourself falling?"

I asked Rebecca during one of our sessions, as I guided her into a Fuel exercise designed to experience the sensation of falling. She didn't answer for a while and continued flowing through the four step cyclical movements that allowed her body to dive forward until her chest hit the mat, press on the palms of her hands to push the hips back into child pose, lift up the torso vertebra by vertebra, and finally rise up to align her hips, shoulder and knees while elevating her arms towards the sky, ready to fall forward and lift herself back up again and again.

"Mad!" she finally yelled after a few rounds. "I hate this...and I hate him. I hate him so much it makes me sick to my stomach."

I asked her to continue moving, to break through that emotion, and reminded her that she was in a safe space. Then when she came toward the end of the exercise I said, "Falling is part of life. So is rising back up and letting go. If you choose to release your resentment towards him, it will never make it right or fair, but it will set you free."

"How?" she asked.

I shared my own experience of forgiveness with Rebecca, and she agreed that seeing herself for the first time would allow her to free the girl who made the mistake of loving the wrong guy, putting him on a pedestal, and making him responsible for her own happiness. So, over the next few months, Rebecca decided to use our sessions together as a way to tackle her own self-forgiveness project. Our practice involved forgiving both minor and major disappointments in her life, starting with the way she related to her own body and movement, to establish a model for the way she dealt with other areas of her life. Minor disappointments were ongoing, small, daily pains that wouldn't stop overnight, and in Rebecca's case, often involved unwanted behaviors around food or exercise— moments like, *I can't believe I just had that muffin. I promised myself I would stay away from sweets*, or *I didn't get my lazy-ass to the gym today*.

The feeling behind those minor sufferings was almost always guilt for doing something that was not aligned with her desire or commitment towards herself. That guilt had to be acknowledged, addressed, and reframed before it would spiral into a cycle of unwanted behaviors and negative emotions. To address that, I gave Rebecca my go-to prayer for quick forgiveness, which, within only a few days of practice, became a simple and effective tool she began to use multiple times each day.

To her surprise, she experienced immediate relief. All Rebecca had to do is observe her thoughts and emotions, witness her disappointment without judgement and release it by reciting the following words: *I recognize that wasn't ideal, but I am more than my mistakes. I choose me and I let that go.* Simple as it may sound, this prayer allowed her to separate herself from the circumstances and imperfect behaviors that made her feel upset, so that her entire day would not be defined by one small event that didn't go as well as it could have. (Remember the story of Christine and the two scenarios she had available? The simple prayer above is what Christine, Rebecca, Nora, and I, continue to use on-the-go to allow ourselves to quickly *choose us* and tune back into journey to free our body)

When Rebecca got more comfortable letting go of the small mistakes, she understood that she needed to release the deep heavy resentment she still felt towards her ex-boyfriend. The only thing stopping her from moving forward, was her own resistance to see that forgiving him didn't mean clearing him from the wrong he had done.

"Rebecca, choosing to forgive him, has nothing do to with him. It only means putting *you* before *him*," I told her. "It's about you, your heart, your time, your energy. If you don't let him go, the only person that you will be punishing is, *you*."

"Maybe," she said. "But I just can't even get myself to say those words."

"Well…don't say I forgive than. Try saying "*I F him!*' see how that feels."

"What do you mean?" she asked.

"Exactly what I just said. Try it :*"I F you, I release you, and I set myself free!*"

Rebecca laughed and nodded as I kept *'F' ing* him, asking her to say it with me. Each time she repeated "*I F him!*" with the intention of releasing him and the rage she felt towards him, she experienced more and more relief.

By all means, it wasn't a serious moment, but for Rebecca, saying those words meant declaring, "I choose *me* before *you*. I am done throwing energy in your direction. I am over punishing myself for what you did. In fact, F you and what you did! Now, let me move onto what truly matters—myself, my desires, my free gorgeous body, and my purpose in life!"

Unorthodox as it may sound, that afternoon, Rebecca got a sweet taste of freedom from the rage, indignation, and sadness that consumed her for months. And that was the beginning of her healing.

At the end of our session, I shared with her the same ritual I had used to release my resentment towards my parents back in Santorini. She didn't comment, but I could tell by her silence that she was not excited about the idea of doing anything like that for her ex, so I didn't insist. Instead, we said our goodbyes, and I told her I'd see her next month when I'd be back to New York City.

A little over two-weeks later, when I was still on the West Coast, I received an unexpected email form Rebecca.

Rakel,

I have to tell you, I thought the whole idea of having a ritual to Forgive Ben was way too out there for me. I couldn't possibly see myself writing him a letter, reading it out loud to myself, burning it, or any of that stuff. In fact, I forgot all about your suggestion and it didn't even cross my mind until this past weekend. It came to me randomly, as I was shopping for my sister's birthday present at Anthropology, and I saw this gorgeous evening gown in my favorite color, emerald green. 'When are you ever going to wear that? I thought to myself. 'You have no special occasions or ceremonies coming up.' Then, suddenly I was like 'Wait! Yes, I do have one.' There it was. I instantly knew the time to move on had finally come and I had to do something about it right away, no matter how weird I felt about the whole thing. So I bought the dress, got home, took a bath, and prepared myself for a date with my feelings that I suddenly felt could no longer wait. I lit the fireplace, put on red lipstick and a few drops of perfume, then slipped into my new, gorgeous gown and sat down in front of the fire with a glass of wine, paper and pen. I took a deep breath and I prepared myself to tell Ben how I felt about him and what I had understood because of him. However, soon after I started writing, I suddenly realized what you had told me all along. All this time, it had been about me, and still it was. I thought forgiving him meant letting him off the hook, saying that it was ok to do what he did, but I could see with clarity that the one I was letting off the hook was—me. I forgave the girl I once was. The girl who needed someone to save her, complete her, and make her feel good enough to be loved the way my father never loved me. I cried tears of grief and joy and when I was done, I stood up, walked to the fireplace, and threw the long letter into the flames. I stood there, watching it burn, until it turned into ashes. I can't possibly express the deep sense of relief I experienced in that moment....Not because losing a man I still love didn't hurt anymore— it does. But because for the first time in my life, I truly felt I came first. I loved me more than it hurt to lose him. I chose me.

By the way, the dress I bought? A size four, which hasn't been my size since college. What is even crazier is that I get to write about this as a final side note to my email, because no matter how happy I am about my new slim figure, I know for a fact that the size of my body does not define my worth. I love to be thin, but I love me more.

Becca

Rebecca's been wearing a size four for the past two years—not that it actually matters. What does matter is that she remains committed to choosing herself, forgiving small and large disappointments, and doing whatever it takes to feel aligned with the person she wants to be in this world. Without a doubt, that means more to her than holding onto what some guy did to her at some point in the past.

GIRL, IT'S ALL ABOUT YOU!

If you were to take away only one thing from this chapter, I hope it would be the notion that *it is all about you.* I know that can sound somewhat selfish. After all, we were told that being generous and kind means being selfless and molding our life to please the world around us. Well, let me make that straight for you: That's a bunch of bullshit! Being self-centered is the most honorable and responsible attitude you can have towards life, and the people around you. The moment you honor yourself before all things, including the mistakes you made or the hurt someone caused you, you become the best possible mother, sister, spouse, friend, teacher, leader, student, citizen, or whatever else you choose to be in this one life. And each time you do that, you create a ripple effect which will benefit those around you, not to mention give you a chance to be fit and free forever.

So, hear me out. No matter how uncomfortable this 4th step might be for you, you can't skip it. *Choose to forgive* is an essential part of your journey to Free Your Body. If you expect the solution to be, *I will never overeat again* or *I'll be forever impeccable with my exercises, or I'll never let anyone hurt me like he did*, then you are bound to be entrapped by the exact disappointment which led you to this issue in the first place—back in your own vicious loop. Remember, I don't want you to lose some weight for a special event, I want you to get in the best shape of your life, from the inside and out, and coexist with your best Self, forever. And that won't happen unless you first soften your own ground, and turn it into a fertile soil to plant the seeds of your desires.

Now keep in mind, we are not looking for perfection, nor are we waiting for one day in the future when you will magically possess the super power of instantaneously letting go of all painful experiences. Learning to forgive is a process, a practice, a journey, which becomes possible the very moment we understand it's all about us. *F the rest!* (Say it with me, if you'd like.) Be brave enough to do it imperfectly, learn to see yourself for the first time, and practice placing your wellbeing before the hurt, the rage, and the past mistakes that are keeping your own soil from being fruitful. You now have all the tools you need. In fact, below are the very exercises I used to help Rebecca. Go through them thoroughly, knowing in your heart that this very step will allow you to raise your energy, boost your creativity, feel lighter, and make your clothes look a whole lot better on you.

As for me, if you happen to come over to my house these days, you'll see that my garden now has six beautiful and healthy fruit trees to remind me that whenever I forgive, I loosen the tight grip anger and resentment have on my life, and I create receptive and fertile soil where life (and plum trees) can grow fruits instead of dust.

SUPPORT WORK

YOUR POWER STATEMENT

*Write down the following power statement and
repeat it as often as you can.*

"When I choose to forgive, I set myself free."

Use this statement any time you feel resentful towards yourself
or someone else, but particularly the times you feel judgmental
towards your body or your eating behavior, or whenever you
begin to dwell on past failures or event. Those fearful moments are opportunities to release whatever is holding you
back knowing that by doing so you set your body free. As soon
as you notice any rage, anxiety, frustration, shameful feelings
towards your self, or desire for retaliation, acknowledge the
thought and without judgement and go straight into your
Power Statement, **"When I choose to forgive, I set myself free."**

YOUR FOUNDATION

Go back to page 106, copy down your Foundation Statement, then take five minutes to add to it any insights you have received from this chapter. Here are some examples: "I choose to believe that I am ready to release all unnecessary weight I've been carrying in my life " or " I choose to believe that mistakes are lessons I don't need to hold onto any longer.". Let this exercise come easily, and trust that if your foundation statement feels good and believable to you, you are good to go. Complete it now:

I choose to believe that I am

_____

_____

_____

Once you've written a statement that feels good to you, copy it down onto an index card, a piece of paper, or on your phone. Make sure you read it frequently, but at least once first thing in the morning, and once last thing at night.

TAKE ACTION

Create your own forgiveness ceremony, just as Rebecca and I did.

It doesn't have to be perfect or final, but do give it your absolute best shot. Some of my clients experienced a quantum shift with their body connection by completing this exercise, while others noticed more saddle shifts over time. Remember, when something doesn't work as we plan, it only means another plan is in the works. With that said, go all in, make it your own, write your letter, burn it and set your Self free.

Change means letting go.

CHOOSE
TO PAUSE

"Listen Leah… I don't think you understand my field." I said to my analyst, as I stretched out on her sofa, my eyes staring systematically at different books, vertically organized in the bookcase in front of me, unable to decipher their titles, rest my body, or find peace of mind. "People want solutions right away. When I tell them that they need to focus on the very step they are in and pause to witness how far they have come, I feel like I'm letting them down."

"Why do *you* feel that way?"

"Because I can't give them exactly what they want," I said. "I know I can help them get the most incredible results, but I cannot do the work *for them*. I cannot believe *for them*. They need to let go of the illusion of fixing themselves first, and I personally know how hard that is. *That* makes me feel terrible."

"Pausing is part of the process. *You* are still resisting, Rakel!"

"No, I am not," I said with assertive confidence. "I get it… really, I am okay with pausing and processing things—"

"—Well…You just said you *feel terrible* telling them they need to pause and witness… And, anyhow, being *"okay with it"* is not enough. You have to fall in love with the notion of the journey, feel inspired guiding your clients to find *their own* connection with stillness and gaining clarity, before taking that next step forward. Only then, will you be able to truly help them."

Silence.

Not another word spoken by either one of us to fill the remaining ten minutes of the session, which, I promise you, felt like ten-thousand years. Leah sat there, said nothing, and allowed me to exist in a space of total discomfort. I was to experience what it felt like to have nothing to fill in my void with and no way to step into the next argument and propel forward. Being without words was rare and unfamiliar. After all, I am the type who could do a double therapy session without running out of things to say or issues to uncover. But not that day. That day, I had no words to say.

"Okay, dear, I will see you next week."

Leah's words concluded those eternal ten minutes, and just like that, I left her office and ventured straight out into the frantic sidewalks of rush-hour New York City traffic. Right there, in the midst of fast-paced movement, anonymity, and chaos was where I always belonged. And yet, as I descended into the subway station below the Time Warner Center and stood among the throngs of people on the overloaded subway platform waiting for my train to arrive, I felt profoundly different. I couldn't put my finger on it, but that long unwanted silence, that awful pause I had just experienced in my therapy session—there was a value to it. That stillness, that void, was extremely uncomfortable, and yet now, having survived it, I felt strikingly present, rooted deep within my body—despite the massive noise around me. I occupied my own tiny spot on that busy platform, felling fully part of everything, without the temptation to analyze it—or even reject—any part of it or myself.

Still, I had no idea how in the world I could possibly communicate what I had just experienced to the women I worked with, but I was certain that after *that pause*, my next action would come with an unprecedented level of clarity and power. Until then, I would practice doing nothing.

SILENCE

Until we learn to pause, we can't clearly see what's standing before us. If you don't think that is true for you, try spinning around the way you used to as a child, and attempt to get a clear image of the moving objects that whir before your eyes. Attempt to feel grounded in your bouncing feet, despite the inevitable dizziness that, sooner or later, takes over your body.

Pausing is essential, and no, it's far from being easy. That is why we resist it so much. Behind the need to keep moving to the next thing, the next lesson, the next chapter, the next book, the next method, objective, drink, or relationship, there is an undeniable fear of being present to ourselves. In the *pause* is where we can honor who we are, stripped down of all distractions—totally empty.

This chapter, this step, is your chance to take a stand for yourself and acknowledge how far you have come from the time you first picked up this book. Maybe you have already started releasing unwanted weight, or maybe you still have a bit more space to clear before you'll have room for your desires to come to life, but without question, today you are far closer to transforming the way you feel about your body, and the food on your plate, than ever before in your life. Today you know that *choosing you*—the *you* that exists beyond your mistakes, your dress size, your trauma, and even your own judgments and opinions—is *the* action that sets the process in motion. It's the decision that cuts off all other possibilities, the willingness to rise above old beliefs, to tune into the present moment, to embrace each step of our journey, knowing it serves a purpose, and to finally release what is not serving you.

Okay… so what's next? you may be asking.

Next, you pause.

Meet Elisabeth.

"So now what?" Liz asked me the day after she burned her letter and watched her mistakes turn into ashes.

"Now, you pause," I said.

Liz was a proud go-getter, and despite the tremendous progress she had made in the past few weeks, she still resisted the idea of stepping back and witnessing what was going on within her body and her emotions, before planning her next move. She wanted to "attack her weight loss mission." Those were the exact words she used to express her determination to fix her body, along with other expressions such as *kill it, crush it, push it, smash it, hit it hard, jump on it, and get it done.* Expressions that, sadly, women use all the time in their approach to fitness. And yes, I have used them myself—*a lot.* There's no doubt that riding such momentum was a winning attitude for a young woman like Liz, but in order for her to make the big shift, to move forward in her journey to get the body she desired and the freedom she deserved…. her actions needed to be backed up by clarity and self-awareness, rather than the forceful and abusive energy that formerly fueled her drive.

"You witness yourself stripped from all that you have released, and honor the new person that is standing before you—the woman who doesn't need to redefine herself right away."

Liz could work as hard and as fast as she wanted to change her body and enrich her life with whatever her heart desired, if those *#goals*, as she called them, didn't become an excuse to keep herself busy, or more importantly, a condition to feel *good enough* about herself. If she wanted to be fit and free *forever* (and she did), then she needed to continue to remind herself that self-worth was her birthright, a privilege she could reclaim at any time simply by taking that first step—choosing herself.

Just like you have done at this point, Liz had already made the first four steps in her Forever journey to Free her Body.

Choose You. Liz had allowed her true self, the woman she knew she was meant to be, to come before her desires.

Choose Now. Liz had enabled her focus to shift to her present reality rather than a happy-ever-after future.

Choose to Trust. Liz had reclaimed her faith in an inner-guidance of her own understanding, allowing herself to embrace her journey one step at a time.

Choose to Forgive. Liz had written a letter and released the resentment she held against her family, herself, and her body.

Thanks to those four steps, Liz could witness a palpable difference in the way she felt about herself and her body and she was excited about her journey. So much so that when I asked her to take time and witness herself, she couldn't keep quiet. She wanted more information and stat. *How long was that pause going to be? When would she take the next move? What would that next move look like and how would she go about it?* Those were only a few of the many, many questions she blurted out to me.

For Liz, pausing meant taking a break from what needs to be done and postponing action. In other words—it was a waste of her time. And, to be honest, I knew exactly where she came from. Almost every single woman I have worked with has resisted the idea of a *non-doing* action, myself included. But I also knew my only way to truly help Liz was to withhold the answers she expected and allow her to experience discomfort and uncertainty, just the way I did years before in New York, when I laid on Leah's sofa for the longest ten minutes of my life. I would hold space for Liz's vulnerability to exist with the right balance of strength, love, and conviction in her ability so that she could experience discomfort, and learn a lesson only stillness and silence can teach.

As a parent of two young boys, my most difficult challenge by far has been to stop myself from making everything okay, and to instead allow my children to feel and own their emotions. It would be so easy to activate my reassuring-mode, to console them right away and say, "Everything is okay. Don't cry! Mommy is here." However, there is a fine line between letting a child know they are supported and safe and allowing him or her to experience and express emotional discomfort. A fine line that I keep working on every single day, because I know without a doubt, that our discomfort zone is where true magic happens, and unless we normalize what's uncomfortable, we end up spending our life running away from our feelings or filling up space with people and things we don't truly want or need—including food.

Choosing to pause gives you the breathing room you need to ask yourself important questions, experience the friction and uncertainty that lives in the gap between your actions, and stay present to your truth even when things are not completely figured out, or when you feel so disconnected that you can't seem to remember who and where you are. It's as if you are saying to yourself, *It's okay. Wait. Let me think about it. The answer will come. No matter what, I am whole, and I am worthy,* before jumping into a commitment you may later come to regret, or taking a step before you are ready for that particular action.

I told Liz that we'd get to her questions later, which again, was hardly the suggestion she was looking for. Then, I walked over to the stereo and pressed play to start our session. I asked her to put her need for answers on hold and just move with me. Use whatever she was feeling in that moment as fuel for her body. She did. Liz grounded herself solid in her feet, activated her core expanding and contracting her ribcage with intention, and exceeded the range of motion of each movement, as if she was trying to grow the perimeter of her body to reach for something she didn't yet know, a new version of herself that was arising from the discomfort of that moment. At the end of what turned out to be a rather intense session that left us both sweaty and out of breath, I asked Liz to drop into Child's Pose, where I explained the breathing exercise we would do next.

"We'll inhale for four counts, hold onto our breath for four counts, exhale for four counts, and hold on to our breath for four more counts, before we start a new breathing cycle."

I guided her through several rounds of that breathing exercise, asking her to focus on the silent pause that exists between each inhale and exhale. When I could sense she had dropped into a deep connection with herself, I spoke again.

"How do you feel, Liz?"

She peeled her head and shoulders up away from her mat, rolled up to sit comfortably on the floor, and looked me straight in the eyes.

"That was *so* difficult," she said, speaking with a deep and calm tone I had yet to encounter in her high-pitched voice. "The focusing on the pause between inhale and exhale... I felt so afraid."

Liz wasn't the first person who felt profoundly uncomfortable paying attention to something so sophisticated and yet so taken for granted as the way our breath works. That pause—that silence, that stillness—that is what exposes us to the infinity of who we are. Yet, in those very moments, all we think about is how fragile and precarious life is. We suddenly become aware that if it wasn't for the next coming breath, our life as we know it, would end. And that of course, can be quite frightening.

"What did you hate about it?" I asked.

"The anxiety I felt having to wait for you to count to four and tell me when the next breath would come. It's almost as if I was afraid there wouldn't be a next breath. And that pause… that silence… it made me feel so… alone, so…I don't know—*empty*?"

Right after she said that word, *empty*, it was as if Liz began searching her mind for the very meaning of it.

"Yeah… empty," she repeated the word again.

The usefulness of cup is in its emptiness
—Taoist Principle

EMPTINESS

Emptiness is a complicated term, which in our modern culture takes on a rather negative connotation. "Containing nothing, lacking reality, not pregnant, marked by the absence of human life, being devoid of sense, and having no purpose or no value," are only some of the definitions we find under the word *empty* in Merriam-Webster's dictionary. With that in mind, it's no wonder we are so afraid to pause and witness the free space within us, so much so that we'd rather fill our plates and our bellies to the max, or overcommit our time trying to do more than what serves us, or makes us happy.

However, there is a completely opposite significance to the word *empty*, one that introduces us to a magical place where everything is possible. In fact, if we look back to 1200 Old English *æmettig* "at leisure, not occupied" or modern Greek *adeios* "freedom from fear," we can see the term emptiness can be applied to a person rather than an object. It that instance, it indicates a privileged individual who enjoys freedom from duties and is therefore unoccupied by worries or fears for the future.

In the light of this new meaning, pausing becomes an *action* full of purpose, a *choice* to place our fears on hold and connect to the part within us that knows everything is possible.

Free space, where eternity lives, just like it does in the pause between inhale and exhale of each cycle of breath.

Think about it for a moment: that pause in our breath is the only human experience we have on this planet of being alive while not breathing, of being *eternal*. Even if we don't pay attention to our breath, we know we are taken care of. For breath happens all by itself, outside of our concern—an involuntary function. However, the moment we choose to focus on the pause, on the empty space between inhale and exhale, we step into our *discomfort zone*. Suddenly feeling naked or exposed by the very land of infinite possibilities. We are eager to occupy empty space with something right away, fill it up as quickly as we can, bring in new things and more actions so that it won't be so... well, *empty*.

Maybe you have experienced this pressure to occupy free space when you moved into a new house and felt the need to decorate right away, or when you started dating right after a breakup, or spent frivolous money right after paying off your credit cards. But nowhere as much as in the realm of food, can we witness the full extent of what happens when we try to avoid emotional discomfort. The spacey sensation of an empty stomach can be extremely disorienting. It can make us feel so vulnerable that we inevitably rush to fill up our bellies, many times well beyond what satiates our hunger. Fill up, rather than witness and understand the signals from our body that regulate our appetite and allow for conscious decisions about what and how much to eat in order to feel and look our best.

Only when we *choose to pause* can we alter the addictive pay-off of compulsive or emotional eating. Simple actions such as taking a few deep breaths to smell the food on our plates before taking our first bite, chewing slowly to truly savor our meal, and putting the fork down after each mouthful to give ourselves time to notice and taste the textures and flavors on our palate, are great examples of practices that apply the notion of pausing to promote awareness, and at times even re-evaluate hunger-signals. For instance, if you feel still hungry right after eating a healthy serving of food, but decide to take a 10-minute pause before going for seconds, chances are that your body will reevaluate your hunger level and you won't feel compelled to fill up your plate again. On the contrary, if you go for that second serving right away, without choosing to pause, you are almost certain to end up stuffing your belly way past feeling satisfied.

The fear of *not having* enough, *not doing* enough, and *not being* enough lives at the very core of our resistance to pause and feel deserving to receive. Whether we attempt to escape the pause in between actions, relationships, goals, meals, mouthfuls, drinks, snacks, or any other compulsive behavior we may engage in, fear of lack convinces us that we need to force our way forward. However, when we choose to pause, we can recognize the truth: Every one of us reading this book is equipped with everything we need to rise and honor what we desire to experience in your lives—including living in a in a fit and free body.

In fact, as long as our beliefs are aligned with our desires, there will always be enough food, space, abundance, opportunity for growth, and love to go around.

HONOR THE NEW YOU

The moment Liz chose to pause, she was able to reconnect with her purpose and prepare to step into the next move with the right intention. For her, this meant taking a day off from her usual routine with a commitment to feel at ease with herself, connect with her breath, and to be as silent as possible for forty-eight hours. During that day, things felt different. The massage she treated herself to, wasn't the usual post workout fix to alleviate soreness. The early morning walk in Central Park, was not an excuse to burn calories. She walked slowly, taking moments for herself to sit on a bench, to breathe and honor her feelings, especially the uncomfortable ones. Whenever she felt hungry, she waited a few minutes to observe her empty stomach with curiosity and teach herself there was no reason to be afraid there wouldn't be a next meal. And whenever she felt anxious, she chose to stay in it, breathe through it, and trust in the process fully. She was surprised to recognize that within a minute or so, the discomfort was still present, but her fear of feeling it was not nearly as intense.

Looks like you survived," I told Liz, a few days after, when she waked into the studio for our weekly session.

"I guess I did." she declared with a smirk on her face. "But I do feel a little strange… I mean, I was happy to come today, but I didn't feel the usual pressure to show up the way I normally do. Does that mean I lost my motivation?"

"No. It only means the work is working. You are letting go of the pressure to do and connecting more with the desire to be."

As the ancient Taoist principle teaches us, "the usefulness of a pot is in its emptiness." Now it's your turn to pause. To honor the new space that you have created for yourself thanks to the hard work you put into the first four steps of this book. This is your time to rise and find the courage to witness that space as it is: empty, free, available, willing, and able to receive new seeds—a magical fertile soil for your fit and free future.

Our own emptiness and our full potential are one in the same. Just like that, the seemingly unimportant moments of stillness are in our lives for a reason. Not to slow us down, but to shine light on the parts of ourselves we are ready to restore. When we do that, we are able to witness ourselves stripped from all that we have released and honor the new woman that is standing before us—one who doesn't need to redefine herself right away.

I can't stress this enough—this fifth step is essential. It is your time to acknowledge how far you have come on your journey and build pressure-free excitement for what is coming. You are finally releasing yourself from food obsession, chronic dieting, and negative body image forever. *Do you get how big that is?*

Remember, it already lives with you, the essence of who you are and what you are capable of accomplishing in your life, and it shows up undisturbed and unnoticed by your thoughts each time you breathe, right in the space between your inhale and exhale. All you got to do, is slow down, hold on to it, and give yourself permission to fully embody it.

Choose to *pause*—with intention, faith and confidence—for this step will give you the clarity and power you need to move forward and witness the mind-blowing changes you desire.

SUPPORT WORK

The goal for this step is to allow you to witness what it means to pause your routine and discon-nect from the part of you that feels on a mission to make things happen. That is why the Support Work for this chapter is different from all others. Here is where I'm asking you to pause on your journey for forty-eight hours, hold on reading the next chapter of this book, or any other books, so that you can shift your focus to honoring your self and your body.

Here are three powerful suggestions to help you integrate this step fully and support you for the next forty-eight hours:

1. **Celebrate what you have learned by buying your-self a gift:** Whether you buy a scented candle, a gorgeous dress, a new pair of shoes, a new lipstick, or fresh flowers, make sure you buy some-thing that feels soothing and somewhat luxurious, while still being within your budget. Light that candle tonight, smell those flowers again, and wear that dress now. Whatever you purchased, in-dulge in it right away, feeling connected to the purpose behind it—celebrating yourself and your body and getting ready to receive miraculous change.

2. **Slow down:** Walk a little slower, take a longer shower, observe silence whenever you can, and when you have to speak do it as slowly as possibly, creating space between each word.

3. **Practice a Meditation to Pause:** You can follow the text below or listen to the audio recording by visiting www.rakelchafir.com/bookresources. Please keep in mind, this meditation is ex-tremely powerful. If you choose to listen to the audio recording, which I suggest you do, plan to find yourself in a setting where you can safely relax. Do not listen while driving or operating machinery.

A MEDITATION TO PAUSE

Sit comfortably on a chair or cross-legged on the floor in an upright position, then close your eyes. Begin to breath in through your nose and out your mouth, noticing how your abdomen expands on the inhale and contracts on the exhale. Observe the breath coming in your nostrils and going out of your mouth. When you feel ready, begin the following breathing exercise while maintaining your starting position with your eyes closed.

Breathe in for four slow counts

Hold your breath for four counts

Breathe out for four slow counts

Hold your breath for four counts

In for four

Hold for four

Out for four

Hold for four

Continue this cycle of breath, slowly shifting your attention to the four counts space that exists be-tween each inhale and each exhale. See if you can extend it by counting even slower. Observe the feelings that come up resisting the need to judge yourself and notice the thoughts passing through your mind, and see if maybe you can experience a small gap between two thoughts where there is no thought. Don't worry if you don't. Just gently focus on the gaps between breaths and between thoughts reminding yourself that in those instants, you are eternal and free. All is possible. All is well.

Whenever you are ready, take a deep breath and open your eyes to the room.

Change comes with stillness.

CHOOSE
TO RESET

"How does it feel? Really…What's it like to be so relaxed around food… at ease with your body…like, *all the freaking time?*" I asked my friend Alison over lunch.

I couldn't wrap my brain around the idea of what it was like to be a woman who had never been on diet and had yet to grow out of her favorite pair of skinny Levi's from senior high. Alison didn't rush to answer, instead she continued to savor her *second* slice of pizza and politely asked the waiter for a box to take the rest home. For a few seconds, I studied her composed posture and undisturbed attitude, then got busy inhaling my chopped salad, mentally questioning if the actual bowl, made of fried tortillas, was something I could get away with eating without bursting out of my spandex.

"Normal, I guess… It just feels …normal," she finally said, as she boxed up her slices. "I mean, I don't always *love* the way I look, but I've never had an issue with it either. I don't see why… should you?"

That was the summer of 2014, and no matter how far I had come in other areas of my life or how many women I had helped with weight loss, I was secretly stressing over food and willing myself into perfect shape. The possibility of being able to stay thin, eat whatever I wanted, and feel that relaxed about my body sounded like science fiction to me. But to Alison, it was *normal*, just a part of her everyday life.

I had never, ever been naturally thin. In fact, I have gained and lost over one-thousand-seven-hundred-and-twenty-five-pounds in my life (remember?). Someone who put on weight as easily as I did, believed that so much as *thinking* about pizza was enough to pack on an extra pound or two. I couldn't possibly grasp that there could be an alternative approach. There was no way I could feel at ease around food, stop fantasizing about the next meal, or *not* be in search of a new strategy to fix my body and help other women do the same. Hell, I couldn't even begin to imagine life without needing to constantly restrain my insatiable appetite, or work my ass off in the gym in order to thwart the inevitable expansion of my thighs. So, no—*I had no idea* how Alison felt. After all, this was 2014, three years before I would spend weeks on my sofa unable to move or breathe properly. Three long years before I'd take that first action of *choosing myself*, which led me to free my body forever.

I had no idea I could become the woman I chose to be, nor had I yet come across the scientific studies that proved it was 100 percent possible.

According to science, cravings, impulses, and what many of us call our "tendency to put on weight easily" are nothing more than strong patterns that we have acquired, which over time have become learned behaviors. This is true even if the rest of your family is overweight or if you have been on a diet since you were a child. Some of these patterns can be so deeply ingrained in our minds, that we have come to believe that they are part of the nature of who we are. Nonetheless, they are not.

Our true nature has nothing to do with what we have become accustomed to do or to believe about ourselves. *Does any of this sound familiar?* I hope so. It's the same concept we addressed in Chapter 1, where we learned that our belief system functions thanks to a number of reference points we have been taught to use as a map, which keeps us going back to the old story of who we are supposed to be. However, what I am about to share with you in this chapter has little to do with the theory of how beliefs work and everything to do with the science that proves permanent change is possible and being fit and free forever is attainable.

On our journey together, up until this moment, we have been more or less directly working on shifting our perception and understanding the forces that come to play behind our actions. In doing so, we have practiced aligning what we think with what we desire and what we feel one moment at a time. Now that we've learned how to do that, we are ready to move one step further, and extend our alignment to our actions and to our habits. Thanks to Step 6, you will understand that unlike other programs, being forever fit and free has nothing to do with controlling your food cravings or becoming impeccable in your behavior. This journey is all about growing into a woman who lives effortlessly in her best body, because she desires only what truly serves her.

Is that even possible? you may still be thinking.

Yes, it is.

Our food choices and our experience of cravings can be reversed by changing the neurological connections in our brain, and there is a term for this, *reset*.

Almost everything will work again
if you unplug it. Including you.
—Anne Lamott

PRESS THE RESET BUTTON

According to Merriam-Webster, the first known use of the term *reset* goes back to 1628, when it was defined as "to set again or anew," and *that* is exactly what we want to do in our relationship to food and body image. Rather than continue in our fruitless attempt to fix our bodies, force our way through diets or restrictive programs that are sure to produce only temporary results, we can start anew by restoring the connections in our brain and reactivating the self-regulating abilities we were born with. To do that, we need to address the control center that monitors and regulates all our physical responses, including hormonal production and programmed behaviors—*our brain.*

However, before we dive into the brain, to gain basic understanding of *neuroplasticity* and how it can help us implement practical changes in our behavioral patterns, I want you to understand that this chapter is not designed to be a thorough scientific account. After reading the following pages you will *not* gain a comprehensive knowledge of how your brain functions and of course, you will *not* gain the expertise of a neuroscientist. I am not one myself, and relaying that information isn't my intention here. I am here—yet again—to show you how your choices can turn your old and unwanted behaviors

164

into new and powerful patterns that support your desires. And for that, I am sharing some very practical tools that you can use. So, now that we have cleared that up, let's look at the very basics of how your brain works and how its functions apply to your relationship to food.

THE BASICS OF NEUROPLASTICITY

Each time you take in new information, your brain sends a message to your nervous system, which creates a connection between two neurons called a *neuropath*. For instance, the first time you respond to anxiety by eating ice cream, you create a new neuropath that links feeling anxious with the consumption of an ice-cold, sweet treat. Whenever you repeat that specific behavior of responding to anxiety by eating ice cream, and the more times you eat ice cream when something triggers your anxiety, the stronger the pattern becomes, and the easier it becomes for you to keep doing it *without thinking about it.* In time, you'll get so accustomed to taking that specific path (eating ice cream whenever you feel anxious) that at the slightest sign of anxiety you'll completely bypass the decision-making process and start walking toward the freezer with a spoon in your hand.

A few minutes later, when you're putting the spoon in the sink, chances are you feel bad about your action and judge yourself for not having enough willpower to make better choices. However, when we look at how the brain functions, you didn't really have much of a choice. With countless neuropaths interconnecting with each other in a complex multi-layered web, all with the purpose of linking feelings of anxiety with the response of eating an ice cream, you didn't stand a chance. You exercised the same behavior enough times, that you automatically by-passed the decision-making process in favor of what has now evolved into an automatic response, a pattern. That is how efficient your brain is.

So, if we've carved a multitude of paths linking the experience of anxiety to the consumption of ice cream, does it mean we're doomed to walk it forever? Of course *not*. But it does mean it's time to use the same patterning process more intentionally, to build a new and healthy automatic response, which will form positive habits around food and feelings that align with our desires. For example (still sticking with anxiety here), if you feel anxious and choose to sip on hot tea and practice a breathing exercise—instead of zombie walking to the freezer, spoon in hand—you will create a new neuropath. Obviously, and especially the first few times, breath-work and hot tea are not going to be as satisfying as eating ice cream would have been, because you are creating only the first few links between anxiety and that particular breathing technique or tea flavor. But the more you'll practice your new pattern (sipping on a hot cup of tea and breathing deeply whenever you feel anxious), the more neuropaths of the same kind will form in your brain, and over time, they, too, will create a strong web of connection. As a result, you'll grow more and more likely to respond to anxiety with the desire to breathe and sip tea. Eventually, breathing deeply and sipping tea whenever you feel anxious, will be your first and most satisfying—automatic—response to anxiety. It will be the response you have without exercising will power or giving it too much thought. Even before the idea of ice cream crosses your mind, you will crave tea and experience a desire to slow down and breathe deep.

I need you to hear this: *Your destiny is not the byproduct of your upbringing or your DNA. It's the aftermath of the choices you make.*

If you choose yourself, tune into the moment, trust your own process, release resentment that holds you back, and take the time to pause before rushing into your next move, you will be able to reset your brain's pattern and watch your body, and your life, become more than what you've ever thought possible. That is not a hypothesis—*it's a promise.*

Meet Amanda.

"I hear you," she said as soon as I told her there was a way to get in shape that didn't involve denying herself the freedom she deserved. "But I have been dieting my entire life. That's just who I am…. I'm used to it. It's really not a big deal for me."

Amanda was resigned to the idea she had to be forever on some kind of diet and never miss a work out. She claimed to be okay with all that, until… well, until she wasn't anymore. A few years after turning thirty-seven, and going through two painful miscarriages, Amanda and her husband began looking into adoption, a process that turned out to be far more complex than they anticipated. After a full year spent going through interviews and filing endless paperwork, a routine doctor's visit revealed that Amanda was almost twelve weeks pregnant. Right there, in that doctor's office, Amanda's priorities shifted, and overnight she became willing to do for her unborn child what she had never done for herself before—slow down, feed herself regularly, get plenty of rest, and take good care of her body. Clear on her desire to have a healthy baby, it wasn't as hard as Amanda had imagined.

However, soon after her baby girl Olivia was born, the stress and pressure she was able to put aside during her pregnancy came back with vengeance. She loved being a mom, but no matter how hard she tried to focus on her daughter and embrace her new life, she couldn't help but feel discouraged about the extra thirty-something pounds of post-baby weight she showed no sign of losing just by breastfeeding. What made matters even more complicated was the guilt and shame she experienced for feeling anything but blessed and overjoyed, as all new moms are too often expected to feel. She had wanted a baby for so long, and now that Olivia was finally in her arms, she couldn't relish in the massive amount of love and gratitude she felt. Instead, she was distracted by the old demons reminding her that her body was out of control and it could only get worst from there.

It was 6:30 AM, and I had just finished a session with a client, when I noticed a text message had popped up on my phone. It was from Amanda.

I know it's early, but can we meet?

A few hours later, at an unusually empty Bouchon Bakery in midtown Warner Center, I gave Amanda a long, heartfelt hug, then I moved closer to the stroller to get a good look at Olivia's chubby little feet as she was sleeping soundly.

"What's going on Amanda?" I asked, as we ordered our lattes.

She kept silent, as if in search for words, then slid her pinky into Olivia's open hand waiting for her tiny fingers to curl around it.

"So much for breastfeeding... If anything, it's making me super hungry."

"I know the feeling," I said as I followed her and the stroller to a corner table carrying a hot latte in each hand.

"It's bad. I mean worse than I am willing to admit," she said as we slid into our seats. "Last night I skipped dinner, told myself I wasn't hungry. Then I woke up in the middle of the night, fed the baby, opened the fridge, and ate everything I could get my hands on. And I mean—*everything.* I felt so gross. I ended up crying myself to sleep."

I kept listening, allowing Amanda to feel free to fully express herself and own her emotions.

"I don't want Olivia to live in the same mental prison I lived in," she said, taking a swallow of her almond latte. "I know what it's like to grow up with an overweight mother who is always depressed...what it does to you, and I can't have that happening to my baby. One way or another, I need to get on a diet and lose this weight, fast... Olivia deserves better."

"So, do you, Amanda," I said. "*You* deserve better."

I knew one thing to be true, if Amanda wanted to be an example for her little girl, her solution could not be found in a diet book or in a workout program alone. She needed to shift her perception, understand her true needs, and stop replacing them with food.

"Here is the thing Amanda, you may choose to follow a diet and loose the extra thirty or whatever pounds you put on this past year. But if you *only* do that, if you *only* lose the weight, then you won't free yourself from the pattern that consumes you, and which will likely hurt your daughter when she grows up. In one way or another—Olivia will learn from you. She will learn from your silence, from your mistakes, from your anxiety, from your tears, but above all, she will learn from the choices you make for yourself, how you feel about your body, and the patterns of behavior you establish around her."

"What are you saying?" she interrupted me. "That I shouldn't lose this weight? Accept my body the way it is? Move on? Focus on all the great things in my life? I promise you... I have tried doing all of that, prayed for it even, but it's not working!"

"You are right, it's not working, but I need you to see that your relationship with your body wasn't working before, either.

Look, Amanda, I have known you for years, and you have always been stressed out about food or missing a workout. So, the answer cannot be there."

"Well…what else can I do?" she asked.

"You can recognize the issue is bigger than your post-baby weight, and that it began the moment you allowed your body to become a measure of your worth."

She looked at me, still not fully convinced.

"Look at Olivia… really, look at her… right now, as she sleeps so peacefully… Isn't it easy to see, she is more than all that? How absurd would it be to think that her worth could be any less or more than another little baby girl because of how much she weighs, how round her belly is, how chubby her thighs are, or how well she burps… *How insane would that be*? Olivia is free, and at one point you and I were that way, too. Your responsibility here is not losing the weight to be in a better mood around her; it's healing yourself so that you can show up fully in her life and set a strong example."

"I would do anything for her… you know that," Amanda said without hesitation.

"Then *choose yourself*, and we can get to work on resetting the very patterns that are keeping you trapped in this prison of yours."

"But I am almost thirty-nine, isn't it a little too late for that?" Amanda asked.

"No, I am asking you to change things you have learned to do, and to believe in, not to change, who you are. If you choose to free your *Self* and commit to resetting your brain, your body and your life can't help but follow."

"At this point I'll try whatever you say," Amanda said, still feeling overwhelmed, but beginning to open up to the idea of trying something new. "But where do I start?"

I opened my backpack, searched through my folders, and pullout a worksheet I had created for a workshop I'd taught earlier that week, a copy of what I was calling my *Forever Fit Guidelines.*

"You start with this."

YOUR NATURAL STATE

Freedom, happiness, and love will always be our natural state. This is true for Olivia, for Amanda, for myself, and even for you. I don't care how messed up, obsessed, afraid, or out of control you feel in this moment. You are not alone, and you do not have to stay in this unhappy loop forever. If you are thinking *It's too late for me,* or *I'll never lose weight,* or *I'll never over-come food obsession,* I am here to tell you something: *You are mis-*

taken. You may feel like *you were born this way*, overeating, body obsessing, and feeling cursed by the tendency to gain weight with tremendous ease, but you were not—Sorry, Gaga!—*you were born free.*

As you know by now, that very first action of *choosing myself*, allowed me to shift my perspective, step outside my narrow vision of what my body could or could not do, and enter uncharted territory to search for a better way to live the life I had always desired. But it is the scientific research that lead me to create the *Forever Fit Guidelines*, that strengthened my faith and fueled my desire to find a practical method for all women who shared a similar challenge in life.

The twelve guidelines I am about to share with you, which I have used to successfully reset my own brain, as well as help countless other women do the same, were designed to help you identify hunger cues and emotional triggers, understand and address your true needs, enjoy food without indulgence, and naturally release excess weight from your body.

If you have followed my directions and completed the Support Work sections in the previous chapters, you'll soon realize that you have already been practicing a few of them. In fact, the whole book so far has been preparing you for this very step. First, you learned how *choose yourself*, connect to the present moment, trust in your own unique process, and release what held you back, so that you could pause and soak into the new powerful awareness of who you are—a woman capable of choosing her own destiny one moment at the time. And now, from this place of newfound clarity, you are ready to witness your physical and emotional reactions to food and body image, create new powerful habits, and restore your self-regulating abilities.

These guidelines will help you create new long-lasting habits that are aligned with your choice and desire to free your body and be fit forever. But remember, unless you continue to practice step 1 to 5, the changes you create will not last. In fact, the power of these guidelines comes forth *only* when you actively practice integrating them all together into your Forever Fit and Free process. That's the only way you can take your transformation to the level of neuroplasticity, and cause biological change in your brain.

THE FOREVER FIT GUIDELINES

Begin your Forever Fit and Free Guidelines practice by integrating each of the twelve guidelines below into your daily life for a period of forty consecutive days. Do your best not to judge the instructions I've laid out for you for you, and at least for this time period (or better-yet forever) do not weigh yourself or measure your body in any other way. As straightforward as they may appear to be, each guideline interweaves with the next, creating a solid groundwork for miraculous shifts.

Keep in mind that like all practices, it will take time to fully consolidate these principles into your daily life. So, don't aim for perfection and impeccability, and allow the five previous steps you have learned on this journey to guide your experience one moment at the time. No matter what, *you*, your self-worth, get to come first.

1. *Whenever you feel hungry, drink a full glass of water and wait five minutes before eating your meal or snack.*

In order to restore our self-regulating ability, we need to get an in-depth understanding of the signals our nervous system receives. This is about training yourself to understand and restore your hunger signals, not about improving your overall body hydration (which is of course important, but not relevant to this point). After five minutes and a full glass of $H2O$, you will know whether you were hungry, thirsty—or perhaps something else entirely.

2. *Eat sitting down at a table (not sitting in a car or in front of the TV or computer) using your favorite plates and the nice silverware that you would normally save for guests or special occasions.*

Not surprisingly, a large amount of overeating happens standing up, in the car, and straight out of a box or a to-go bag. When we decide to turn our meals into a ritual to celebrate and nourish ourselves, we inevitably change the intention and the energy behind our actions. Remember, it's not *what* we do, but *why* we do it and *how* we go about it. So, before you take your first bite, practice saying out loud, "I choose me, and I choose this meal to honor myself and my body."

3. *Eat only when you are hungry.*

Practice asking yourself the following five questions before eating:

Am I hungry or angry? Hungry or tired? Hungry or lonely? Hungry or sad? Hungry or bored?

Understanding when and why we are driven to eat is essential to our transformation process, so stay committed to answering the above questions even if, at first, you won't be able to alter your behavior. For instance, if you recognize that you respond to being upset by eating larger meals, you can choose to express your feelings, or reach out to a professional who can help you address and heal the wounds which live beneath your anger; or if you know your tendency is to overeat when you are bored, you can reach out to a friend, go for a walk, cultivate a new hobby, and make *having fun* a priority in your life.

4. *Eat only until you are satisfied.*

Most of us have no idea how to discern a sense of satisfaction from a sense of fullness. That is because we have trained our body to alternate between feeling deprived and being rewarded with over indulgence. To help you restore your natural self-regulating ability, I have included the hunger scale right below, a practical tool you can use to learn how to recognize your hunger level. By using the scale, you will soon identify how feeling bloated, stuffed, tired, or uncomfortable is a signal you have eaten beyond satisfaction level. While enjoying fully, each mouthful and taking a pause between bites, will allow you to experience pleasure, wellbeing and satisfaction. Eventually you will understand these signals in depth, and that ability will enable you to stop and start eating within the right range for your body.

1	Beyond hungry. You feel weak, have no energy, and feel the need to lie down.
2	You feel sick to your stomach with very little energy.
3	You feel your stomach is empty and the desire to eat is strong.
4	You start to think about food and you feel a little hungry.

5	You're just starting to feel full enough.
6	You're completely satisfied.
7	You're beyond the point of satisfaction but not yet uncomfortable.
8	You're starting to feel uncomfortable.
9	You're uncomfortable and starting to feel sluggish.
10	Beyond full. You are physically in pain and feel the need to lie down.

–Between 3 and 6 is the ideal time to start and stop eating.

5. *Taste and enjoy your food fully.*

After each bite, place the fork on the table to focus on chewing and savoring what you are eating. You can eat absolutely anything you want—*as long as you absolutely enjoy every single mouthful.* This one is tricky for you may think you love food. However, shoving food down your mouth and swallowing it as fast as you can doesn't mean you are tasting it or truly enjoying it. The challenge here is to *savor* each bite by noticing the textures, spices, and sensations on your palate as if you had to describe them to someone else. The simple act of putting down your fork after each mouthful will help you break the pattern of eating quickly, while simultaneously allowing you to fully connect with the feeling of pleasure, and sending a message to your brain that you are satisfied, and don't need to eat any more food.

6. *When you eat, only eat.*

Do not attempt to do anything else—*I know, this one is so hard*—such as watch a movie check your email, read a book, send text messages, or go on social media. Put your cellphone on silent. Shut off your TV. Close the book. Yes, even this book! Make a commitment to nourish yourself, and your body, without distractions. If you are eating with others, take your time to assess your feelings, join the conversation, and observe your reactions. You may find that eating with someone makes you feel connected or that instead it may be a way for you to check-out from the present, from an uncomfortable feeling, or from your own *Self.* Do your absolute best to practice this exercise without judgment, and always remember that your only task is becoming your own witness and staying committed to *choosing yourself* one moment at the time.

7. *There is always more available that I can eat later. There is no lack around me.*

To restore our body's optimal functionality and release excess weight with ease, we need to change the messages we send to our brain from, *there is never enough*, or *I can't get enough*, to *there is always plenty available*. Each time we are on a diet, or stressed over food, we send a clear message to our brain: *there is only so much food to use as energy, and you may not get what you need*. This message in turn, activates the most primitive part of our brain, perceiving the presence of danger and not understanding that the lower energetic intake and the constant mental stress that comes with it, is nothing more than a self-inflicted torture, designed to drop a few inches off our waistlines. Feeling under attack and not knowing when or if the next meal will come, your body slows down and holds onto fat storage, in case you'll need it in the future to convert into energy and keep yourself alive. On the contrary, once you become present to the abundance that is available to you, there will be no reason to feel in danger, to stuff yourself beyond what your body truly needs, and to hold onto fat storage for survival.

8. *Replace using the word 'losing' weight with 'releasing' weight.*

The words we use impact our lives more than we realize. If you lose weight, chances are you will regain it. According to Merriam-Webster's dictionary, *to lose* means, *to miss from one's possession*, or *to suffer deprivation of something*. When you say you lost weight, you claim that you have lost something that belonged to you—it was yours to have. On the other hand, *to release* means *to set free from restraint* or *to give up*. With this book, you learned that the extra weight is not *you*, it does not define *you*, and therefore you have no reason to hold on to it. It is something you can afford to release from your life, forever. Don't lose it, *release it*.

9. *Each time you see your reflection in a mirror, or a window repeat to yourself, "I choose me."*

It may feel awkward the first ten times you do it, but *I promise* you, it will become second nature. Remember I'm not asking you to look at your reflection and tell yourself "I am beautiful," or "I am thin." Not even "I am losing (releasing!) weight." Those are the consequences of choosing yourself, not the actions that will get you there. Each time you face your reflection and make that choice, "I choose me," no matter how you feel or how you look, you release the pressure to be anything that you are not, and send a powerful message to your brain that all is well, there is no need to stress or try to eat our *Selves* out of feeling not good enough. *Choosing yourself* effects your appetite, lowers your stress hormones, and makes you more inclined to do what is best for you and your body—*do it*.

10. *Eat what makes your body feel good.*

Here is the deal, *do not* exclude processed and sugary food because in your mind they are forbidden or classified as bad. I can't stress this enough: *you cannot be on a diet or food restriction to free your body forever.* When you *choose yourself,* you ultimately will choose to avoid ingredients you feel have a negative impact on your energy level and your emotional health, but it *must* be a choice absent of any form of judgment. Personally, I don't do well with sugar, gluten, and dairy products. They make me feel bloated, constipated, and undeniably uncomfortable. So, I don't even want to eat them on a regular basis. I found many of my clients (not all of them) share a similar reaction to those substances while other feel better eating plant-based meals or not consuming caffeine at all. (Not me! I need my coffee!) If you are uncertain about following this guideline correctly, the one method that always works is simply asking yourself the following question, "Is this food choice honoring me and serving me? Do I feel good whenever I eat this?" You'll have your answer.

11. *Move twenty minutes every day in ways that brings you joy.*

I don't care if you go up the stairs of your building four times, go to a barre class, take your dog for a twenty-minute walk, dance alone in your underwear (I highly recommend), practice yoga, become an avid Soul Cycle rider, or a tango dancer. All I care about is that you move—every day—for a sustainable time and enjoy doing it. The twenty-minute walk you take while grocery shopping will always be more effective than the four-mile run you never make time for.

12. *Acknowledge your progress—no matter how tiny it might be.*

Believe it or not, noticing your behavior without being able to modify it, is progress. It represents a necessary step towards your freedom, and you must acknowledge yourself for it. Take the time to acknowledge yourself whenever you are able to distinguish physical from emotional hunger, or remember to drink a full glass of water five minutes before your meal. Take pride in going for that 20-minute walk, setting the table for yourself, or having the courage to repeat the magical words, "*I choose me,*" when you look in the mirror. It's progress, not perfection, that we are always shooting for. Know that every single time you acknowledge your progress, you strengthen your trust and align with your desire to be fit and free forever. The little boost of confidence you will give yourself today, acknowledging that you were able to put down your fork after each mouthful over lunch, will give you the motivation to sign up for a yoga class you love four times next week. Every little action counts and multiplies.

TASTE YOUR FREEDOM

I told Amanda that if she followed the *Forever Fit Guidelines* for forty days, and remained committed to choosing herself, she would witness miraculous shifts in the way she ate, moved, felt, and looked.

"*Why forty days?*" she had asked.

"Forty days is the average amount of time it took most women I worked with to form new, automatic, responses and feel at ease with their new habits," I explained. "Besides, it's approximately the amount of time it took me to experience a real shift. Give it a try!"

Over the first couple of days, Amanda and I spoke frequently. Then, I traveled to Europe and we lost touch for a few weeks. The next time I heard from her I was back in the city, and it was, once again, early morning. However, this time, the nature of her call was quite different.

As soon I picked up the phone and heard Amanda's voice, I knew the work was working. Amanda sounded excited, cheerful, completely different from the woman I had spoked with a little over a month before.

"I *had to* call you and tell you what just happened to me." she said. "It's not a big deal, so don't get excited. But it's just a big deal for me."

"Go on. Spit it out."

"Ok…Here it is. I was just in the kitchen. By myself. Having the best time making my breakfast. Spreading this gorgeous avocado on a piece of perfectly toasted sprouted bread, then sprinkling little bites of chopped tomatoes all over it as if it was fancy cake decoration. Right there and then, as I was ready to take a seat and eat, I caught a glimpse of myself in the large mirror that hangs over the kitchen table. Dude, I was *smiling—at myself, for no reason… feeling happy to meet my eyes.* Not because I thought I looked good…*God, I haven't even brushed my hair yet!* And certainly not because I was telling myself to do it. It was accidental…automatic… feeling good about me felt… I don't even know how to say it… *normal.*"

In a little over a month, Amanda had made tremendous progress. She had learned to feel connected to her body and distinguish the times she felt physically hungry versus those she was emotionally triggered. By doing that, she noticed her tendency to respond to her need to rest and take some time away from the baby, with mindless eating. Soon after she became aware of that, she had arranged for friends and family to help her, so that she could slowly begin to feel better, and as a consequence, feel less hungry and less inclined to overeat. Amanda listened to my suggestion and got rid of her scale, but it was undeniable— she was releasing weight and looking healthy and happy. But here is the best part. Thanks to her practice, Amanda felt inspired about life and more positive about her future. Overall, she felt naturally drawn to eat nourishing and energizing meals, cook more, and become more creative. She learned to reach out for help, and she remained committed to her own healing process, understanding the best way to care about her daughter was to care about herself. It wasn't always easy, but even the times she forgot about the guidelines or indulged in her cravings, Amanda learned to quickly bounce back to choosing herself so that she could re-align with her commitment to set her body free and become a powerful example for little Olivia.

Just like Amanda did, by practicing the *Forever Fit Guidelines* for forty days and integrating them with the first five steps we have walked together on this path, you too will be creating new neuropathways, which in time will result in biological changes in the way you think, act, and look, forever. Before you know it, you *will* notice yourself eating less, enjoying your food more, releasing weight naturally, and doing so without stress. Eventually, choosing you, eating sensibly, and moving in ways that honor your body and bring you joy, will become second nature, something you do effortlessly without giving it too much thought and without any internal conflict.

2014 wasn't that long ago, and yet, there I was, the girl who always cleaned up her plate and left the table wanting more; the girl who thought living a life free from food and body obsession would not be possible for her—not unless she gave up on being fit or looking good. Five years after that, after going through my second pregnancy, and quite a few other challenges you already know about, I have no idea of how much I weigh. I choose not to put a number on my body, and I suggest you do the same. And guess what? I have been fitting into my favorite pair of skinny jeans without growing out of them. In fact, I've never looked or felt better in my life, not even in my twenties.

I want you to have that for yourself, to know how it feels to be *naturally* in your best shape, relaxed around food, and to believe this feeling is normal and available to you because you choose it. This step is what will make it possible.

Can you begin to see it for yourself? Taste that freedom?

Our journey together has been about remembering who you are, putting that incredible woman first, releasing old resentment, and forgiving past mistakes so that you, *yes you*, can reclaim the space you need to reconnect to your truth. And now you are here, ready to take step six, choose to reset—backed by science itself—the step that will help you build new powerful habits and become more than you ever thought possible. So, go ahead, step in fully, press the *reset* button, and know with absolute certainty that you are well on your way.

SUPPORT WORK

POWER STATEMENT

*Write down the following power statement
and repeat it as often as you can.*

"I choose to reset my brain to get in the best shape of my life."

Use this statement whenever you witness a less-than ideal be-havior around food, noticing whether you have been triggered by anxiety, stress, frustration, boredom, fatigue, or even excite-ment. Right there, as you begin to experience cravings, stop whatever it is you are doing and recognize the presence of an opportunity to choose. Quickly repeat your power statement to yourself: **"I choose to reset my brain to get in the best shape of my life."**, then ask yourself, *is there another way I could respond to this right now?*

Trust that asking your self this question will begin to shift your relationship with food even if ini-tially you might not be able to stop yourself from engaging in any specific automatic response you have developed over the years, and know in your heart, that your ability to acknowledge your be-havior and practice your power statement, is enough to help you move forward. This is a very deli-cate process, so be extra gentle with your self and don't forget to choose you one moment at the time.

YOUR FOUNDATION

Go back to page 134, copy down your Foundation Statement, then take five minutes to add to it any insights you have received from this chapter. Here are some examples: I choose to believe that I am actively changing my brain and getting in the best shape of my life", or "I choose to believe that the twelve guidelines will set me free forever". Remember to take no more than five minutes to com-plete this exercise and write something that feels believ-able and good to you. Complete it now:

I choose to believe that I am

_____

_____

_____

Once you've written a statement that feels good to you, copy it down onto an index card, a piece of paper, or on your phone. Make sure you read it frequently, but at least once first thing in the morn-ing, and once last thing at night.

TAKE ACTION

You now know, all those little actions you have been taking in the first four chapters were part of a set of guidelines that have the power to rewire your brain and cause miraculous changes in the way you relate to your body and to your life. From this step on, you will be asked to practice using all 12 Forever Fit guidelines to reset your and restore your self-regulating abilities.

I can't stress this enough; the repetition of these guidelines is the key to transform your relationship with your body so that you can effortlessly stay fit and free forever. So do not lose momentum or miss out on your opportunity to practice for the next 40 days. In fact, start right now. In this mo-ment. Can you get up and get a glass of water? Or maybe, dance around your house for twenty minutes?

For your convenience, you can access a printout of the guidelines at rakelchafir.com/bookresources

Change means being willing to start over.

CHOOSE
TO RECEIVE

Over the course of my life, I had heard my father rave about
his aunt Sarah's famous *boeuf à la Bourguignonne* so many times,
that when I finally sat at her table and saw the steam coming
from the large *casserole*, I closed my eyes, inhaled the warm aro-
ma, and witnessed my mouth watering in anticipation. Right
in front of me was a feast of seductive h'ors dévores, terrines
and pâtés, creamy balls of Normandy salted butter, and crispy
slices of fresh baguette straight from my favorite *boulangerie* on
Rue de Lepic, and yet unlike the other guests, which included my
husband, my parents, and my two kids, I rested both my hands
on my lap and waited for the extraordinary stew to make its
glorious entrance. It wasn't one of those times I felt compelled
to "pass on bread-and-butter to avoid carbs" or "skip on finger
food to manage my caloric intake." In fact, I didn't even think
about any of that. By then, I had felt free in my body for over
a year, and clean-eating—without dieting—had turned into a
normal way of life, a *habit* that required no effort on my part.

I had learned to consistently tune into the moment without second-guessing my actions or judging myself for my choices. So, as I sat there, knowing that I was choosing to fully savor something that took nine long hours and a massive amount of love to prepare, I felt at ease with my surroundings and connected to myself. I wanted to receive the experience fully, and nothing—not even delectable, calorie-infused French bread—could stop me.

After Aunt Sarah placed the steaming *casserole* at the center of the table, she took the seat right beside me. If it wasn't for the deep and sagging lines in her face that formed her gentle expression, I would have never believed she had just turned ninety-six. In fact, she moved with more ease than most people twenty years younger and spoke with an echo of youth I'd never heard before in someone so close to a century old.

"Viens, Melinda, viens…s'il te plait," she said. *Come, Melinda, come please.* "Le beuf…il faut servir le beuf quand c'est bien chaud." *The beef…we must serve the beef now that is hot.*

Spoon in hand, I watched as Melinda slowly poured the stew into my bowl—its rich, dark-brown color clashing against the white porcelain of Aunt Sarah's gorgeous china. I inhaled deeply before I carefully dipped my spoon into the gravy to capture just the right balance of meat and broth before raising it to my mouth. The first bite of succulent beef sent my tongue into a frenzy. I didn't even need to use my teeth. It melted like butter, allowing me to savor each individual ingredient in that spoonful of heaven: thyme, garlic, onion, ground black pepper, fresh mushrooms, possibly beacon, and delicious red wine. All of those flavors masterfully coming together into a unified rich texture, so divine, that I wished every single mouthful could last forever. As I returned my attention to the room, I noticed that Aunt Sarah wasn't eating. She was looking straight at me instead.

"Ça me fait plaisir de te voir manger comme ça," she said. *It's a pleasure to watch you eat like this.*

Her words came unexpectedly, and it took me a few moments to catch myself and shift from what would have otherwise been the usual reaction of shame, anger, and anxiety that I experience whenever someone had the audacity to comment about the way I ate.

"Merci. C'est délicieux. Préparé avec beaucoup d'amour," I said. "Quel honneur de le recevoir!" *Thank you. It's delicious. You made this with so much love. What an honor to receive it!*

Aunt Sarah smiled as if she knew exactly what I meant by feeling honored to fully receive the gift of life that was bestowed upon me in the form of a hand-cooked meal, to allow that stew to feed my body as well as my soul, and to use such an intense experience of pleasure as a powerful instrument to connect with myself and my body.

Such is the power of receiving.

Women's pleasure is the greatest
untapped resource in the world
—Regina Herman.

RECEIVING VERSUS TAKING

From the Latin *recipere*, *re-* "back," + *-cipere*, "to take," the original meaning of *to receive* was, *to return to and make whole again*. Although it is often used interchangeably, *receiving* does not have the same energy as *getting*, *taking*, or *obtaining*. Instead, there is an element of trust and faith involved in receiving, a willingness to allow something to evolve as it should and impact our lives fully, rather than *taking possession* of it, or *grabbing it by the horns* to use it as we wish. The difference lies in the intention behind what we do, why we choose to do it, and how we choose to go about doing it. *Sound familiar?* It is the very principle behind every single step we have taken together on this journey and every single choice we made along the way.

When we choose to receive and to satisfy our true needs, we learn to relate to our body with the intention to honor it rather than manage it, punish it, or control it. And by doing so, we place ourselves in the most efficient position to eradicate the urge to overeat, so that we won't need to fight our cravings or control our behaviors to begin with. That, right there, is true freedom.

Meet Nina.

Since she was a teenager, my good friend Nina ate very little in front of friends. The other girls and I used to be jealous of her almost inexistent appetite, and never in a million years did we consider her behavior to be anything else other than a lack of interest in food. I have to give it to her, because over the course of my life, I have seen hundreds of girls who struggled with various kinds and degrees of eating disorders, but to this day, I have never seen anyone who could cover up her issues as effortlessly as Nina. In fact, if it wasn't for what she revealed to me almost 20 years later, I would have never suspected that all those days when she left me at my favorite gelato spot, or passed on pizza night at my house, she'd go home, fill up her plate with leftovers from her fridge, sneak upstairs to her room, and eat alone in hiding.

Nina and I had lost touch for a number of years, but then randomly reconnected at an event for female entrepreneurs, where I had been invited to speak on success from a mind and body perspective.

"Thank you!" Nina said, giving me a heartfelt hug as soon as my presentation was over. "When you shared your story with us, about realizing there had to be another way to live other than spending most of our time thinking about food and feeling ashamed for feeding ourselves, experiencing pleasure, and desiring to feel satisfied and all that, I felt like you were seeing right through me. I had heard those same things a million times before, and yet, for some reason, I had never truly heard them until today."

That night I learned that my friend Nina had been a closet eater since she was only ten. Not only that, but never in her life had she felt comfortable receiving anything—not a compliment, a gesture of kindness, someone's attention, a gift, and of course, never the food on her plate. Her adult life looked pretty good on paper. She worked for a successful design firm, had an active social life, and belonged to a large circle of friends that she periodically invited over to her house for exquisite dinners and fancy social gatherings that never ceased to amaze. Her eye for color and beauty came through every single element she placed on her table. From the most delicate flower arrangements, fine linens, fancy crystals, and artsy ceramics to the actual meal—a feast of delicacies she'd prepared, cooked from scratch, and barely tasted herself. At least not until everyone left.

"You know how particular I am about cleaning," she'd say when a friend offered to wash a dish or wipe a countertop after dinner. "You guys go home… really. I like to take my time and do it on my own."

Once everyone was gone, Nina would stand alone in the middle of her messy kitchen, surrounded by leftovers, unseen by the world, and eat up what her guests had left behind. One bite after the other until there was nothing left.

"It's so humiliating," she said to me, referring to her secret behavior. "Sometimes over dinner, while I sit and talk to someone, in the back of my head all I'm thinking is, *When will you all leave so I can get to eat?*"

After Nina and I reconnected, we met for coffee on several occasions, where I observed her apologizing for taking my time, insisting on paying for my hazelnut cappuccino, and repeatedly shifting the conversation to highlight what was going on with *my* life, *my* work, and *my* family. Never once would she acknowledge herself or speak about her own feelings or the projects she was working on in her life. And whenever I made a positive comment about her, no matter how small, she was quick to downplay it with remarks such as, "Oh, that's nothing" or "That's really easy to do." And every single time we met it was, "No. Let me pay for it. It's the least I can do. I know how busy you are."

Now, I can guess what some of you may be thinking (and I agree), that there are far worse things one could do in life than give too much. But trust me, being a compulsive giver isn't such a noble act, and I want to show you how many of us use a variation of what I like to call "funky giving" to avoid feeling vulnerable enough to receive. Even if your impulse to give to others or shift the attention away from yourself is not as drastic as Nina's, or if you have a tendency to engage in exactly the opposite behavior (such as making everything about you), there is something important you can learn from her story. Playing the role of the *caretaker* and the *best listener* gave Nina the illusion of being needed, while not needing anyone or anything in return. Behind all of her generosity and kindness, she was able to hide her true intention. Nina wanted to maintain control, avoid vulnerability, compensate for her lack of self-worth, and prevent people from having a real impact in her life.

Although in reality we all need each other to function at our best, the illusion of being self-sufficient makes us feel in control. Think about it for a moment. If you were the one always inviting me, complimenting me, supporting me, caring for me, and providing for my every need, then you would put me in the position of always owing you. As a result, I would never be able to participate equally in our friendship. If I was to lose you, you'd think I would lose someone of great value, someone I needed. *Right?* But if you were to lose me, it wouldn't be too much of big deal. *Would it?* In light of that, we can say that positioning ourselves as the giver is yet another way to play safe and feel somehow superior to those we are giving to. And as innocent as this kind and supportive behavior may appear, compulsively giving is not fair play, and it doesn't truly serve anyone involved—not the giver and not the receiver.

It sure wasn't easy, but I decided it was time to talk to my old friend about how I really felt. We met at our usual spot, ordered our cappuccinos, and walked towards what had become "our table" in the far back corner of the cafe. As we sat down—before Nina could open her mouth to ask me how I was doing and shift the conversation to make it all about me—I asked her to look at me straight in the eyes and prepare herself to listen to what I had to say. *Without interrupting me.* Nina had no clue what I had in mind, and I could tell how nervous and uncomfortable this made her feel.

"You are my friend," I said, "and I need you to know that the way you feel, the things you do, the challenges you experience—they matter to me."

She nodded her head and looked down, completely dismissing what I was saying, yet she was afraid to stand up and beg me to shut up, as much as she wished I would.

"I need you to hear this, so I will say it again—but this time, look at me straight in my eyes and listen. The way you feel, the things you do, the challenges you experience—*they all matter to me*. You don't need to make every moment about me. In fact, the kindest thing you could do is trust me and allow my words to reach you by receiving them… *Being open is the greatest act of generosity.*"

Nina said nothing. She looked away for a long moment, attempting to hide her reddening cheeks behind her slim fingers, as if she wanted the earth to open up and swallow her whole. I could tell she was mortified.

"It's okay," I said. "You can let your body react freely. I promise I don't have an opinion about it, and neither should you. This place is empty. It's just us and our cappuccinos… so you are safe."

"I don't know what to say," Nina said after a while. "I mean, I just like listening to you and learning about all the amazing things you do… that's all… and I love doing things for others! Isn't that a good thing?"

"Well," I said, "If you truly want to do something nice for others, stop holding back on yourself. Share how you feel and what is going on in your life. Allow people to feel free *to see you, to reach you*, and *to care for you.*"

"I'm just trying to do my best." She said before letting out a long, defeated sigh.

"Stop. For God's sake, stop doing your best and start being your most."

"What do you mean? *Stop doing my best?* What good would that do?"

"I mean stop making your life about pleasing others. Stop being *perfectly* lovely and start being imperfectly *you*. Be generous enough to receive something from someone else."

As I spoke to Nina, I found myself unable to sugarcoat what I still believe in 100 percent. I wanted my friend to know that being anything less than who she is, means being a disservice to the world. The same is true for you. Every second the clock is ticking and we are not ourselves, we take away our true presence from the world and obstruct it from the people in our lives—people we could instead serve by offering a powerful example of a woman committed to stand in her own light and own her truth. Look around you, at your own life, do you see how hard we all work to avoid thinking we have a limited amount of time in this one body? Sure, it's not comforting to know that we are precarious, fragile, and unable to control the moment we'll unavoidably make a final exit from this dimension of life, but only by facing the fact that we won't be here forever can we understand the urgency to use our time to become whoever the hell we are meant to be, without wasting one more second dwelling on whether or not it is worth the risk, or if we deserve it.

So, no, my conversation with Nina wasn't the most gentle, but I was unwilling to put up with my friend's decision to play the part of the perfect host and the kindest friend for one more second. I couldn't sit there and watch her renounce to fully living the incredible journey she deserved to experience—just so that she could feel safe and comfortable.

After I spoke, we sat in silence for a long while. I tried to remain calm, holding myself back from comforting her, diverting the pressure, or even shifting the conversation to put an end to the awkward moment we were both experiencing. I wanted her to hear me, but I knew my words alone wouldn't do it unless she allowed herself to experience what it meant to temporarily lose control, and realize that her safety didn't depend on it. Nina needed to know that she could break down and be supported, that she could be imperfect and still be loved, and that she could receive fully and still be needed.

"We'll sit here for as long as you need." I said, unable to keep quiet myself. "As long as it takes for you to know that I support you, whether you just want to breathe in silence or tell me what's on your mind. There is *nothing* you could possibly do or say that would make me think any less of you."

More silent minutes ticked by, and I noticed the tension began to fade from her body. Her posture became softer, and a different, more relaxed, energy began to emerge between us. Nina was in her body, sitting at our table, in front of her now cold cappuccino, allowing herself to receive my imperfect yet undeniably heartfelt support, and knowing that I wasn't going to settle for anything less than connecting with the real woman in front of me. That moment wasn't perfect, but it was real, it was fully received, and it served us both greatly.

THE MOON OF LOVE

The sun is the wine; the moon is the cup.
Pour the sun into the moon if you want to be filled.
– Sufi poet Hafiz

In Sufism, the second pathway of the heart is called *Ar-Rahim,* The Moon of Love. On this path, in order to unite to our beloved, we are called to experience our own full capacity to receive love, and we are invited to look to the moon to learn how to stop resisting. *When the moon is full, the light that bounces off of it illuminates our world.*

"La Luna!" my son William calls her, as he reaches out his index finger to point at the night sky, as if calling out to the mother of all stars.

Even my youngest, Donovan, who is not even speaking yet, will point his tiny hand toward the night sky. It's not hard to see why it's so comforting to a child to know the moon is there, discontinuing that vast darkness and safeguarding the night, just like a mother does with a small child. Yet the most interesting thing about the moon, and the reason why it relates so well with this last step of our journey, is the fact that *she* (yes, I like to think of the moon as a female) does not produce *her own* light. She shines because her surface reflects the light from the sun.

Just like the moon, when we are able and willing to receive light and energy from a source of our choice, our cup runneth over, our stomach feels satisfied, and the light within us becomes enough to reflect our moonbeams onto everyone and everything around us. Whether it's a message, a lesson, a meal, a seed, an orgasm, a gift, or an idea, the art of receiving is the greatest act of generosity you could choose, because the moment you learn to receive and feel satisfied, you become a better mother, a kinder daughter, a more sensual lover, a more sincere friend, a wiser leader, and all-around greater human.

Look back at a time when you were in love, and you felt truly satisfied and appreciated by a partner. Remember how that affected other areas in your life. How you suddenly felt the impulse to be kinder to people, smile more, start a project, and even eat more sensibly. Now think about the exact opposite situation. Consider for a moment, how a frustrating relationship you experienced in your past effected the way you felt about yourself and influenced your overall performance in life. If, for example, you were living with a self-centered partner, or if you worked for an abusive boss, chances are you'd feel frustrated and anxious most of the time. You might snap at your kids, ignore a friend in need, and walk around de-motivated by a world filled with lousy people and unfair circumstances—a world you wish you could escape. In fact, that is exactly what you try to do when you walk into the pastry shop on your lunch break and treat yourself to a little sweet to numb the stress of denying yourself the love, fulfillment, and joy you deserve to receive. Of course, there is nothing wrong with consuming the sweet, but there is so much harm in the reason why you do it — covering up your true needs because you don't actually believe you deserve to satisfy them.

So I need you to hear this and to hear it now: Unless you decide that you deserve to receive everything that you desire— for no specific reason other than the fact you are breathing— sooner or later, you will feel the need to prove your own worth, which will compel you to sabotage your goals, retreat from your path, and resist the real change you long for in your body and in your life. From there on, it will be only a matter of time before your old reference points come back to surface and your old behavioral patterns around food go back to replace your newly acquired freedom.

But if you give yourself permission to receive fully, because you decide that you deserve nothing less than complete satisfaction, you will experience true freedom and ease, including when it comes to your relationship to food. Clear about your worth and free from self-doubt, you will be naturally guided to make consistent choices that honor your body, such as eating what makes you feel good, moving in ways that bring you joy, and staying committed to choosing yourself one moment at the time. Remember, unlike other programs, our journey together has never been about developing mega strength or using Navy Seal willpower to control our behavior around food. Step after step, we have been working on mending the internal conflict that consumed you for years, and making powerful choices that cannot coexist with the urge to overeat or the impulse to sabotage your own efforts. With no resistance to fight against, no cravings to control, no rules to break, no mistakes to feel bad about, no perfect future to trip on, or resentment to hold on to, you will have no other option but to *succeed*.

PERMISSION TO HEAL

Months after our uncomfortable conversation, Nina found the courage to open up to the idea of receiving help. She joined a support group, found an excellent therapist, and eventually shared her life-long struggle with binge eating disorder with her closest friends, who were all open and happy to support her. From that moment on, whenever they met, Nina didn't get to host, decorate, cook, serve, or clean up after them. All she could do is show up, in all her vulnerability and with all her imperfections, and allow others to treat her like the guest of honor. Her progress was undeniable, and yet Nina's journey to free her body had only begun.

I am going to therapy, meetings, talking more openly about my feelings…but I've got this fear…this anxiety whenever I think about food or sit down to eat…I just don't know how to fix that," she told me when we met at our usual spot, months into her recovery.

"You can't fix it." I said. " But you can heal it." That's when I shared with her the seven-steps method you have been practicing in this book.

"It comes down to seven powerful choices that can help you shift your relationship to food and your body forever." I then went on to list and briefly explain each step, until finally, I got the last one, *choose to receive…*

"Wait!" Nina interrupted as I introduced her to Step 7. "Isn't that where I started… with receiving?"

"Yes, you did," I said. "We all do. The very first moment we choose ourselves, we do so because we have received something. It could be a guidance, a lesson, an experience, a hint, anything that guides us to that deep knowing that we deserve better. The moment you heard my talk, something happened within you that made you walk over to me and tell me about your secret. That moment initiated everything else you have done this past year. And that was only possibly because that night, for whatever reason, you received my words and you *chose yourself* over the fear of being judged."

So here you are, at the last of the seven steps to *Free Your Body*—choose to receive. And yes—without you knowing it—you have been practicing this final step from the very first page of this book.

Being able to take in a lesson and fully receive it without quickly diverting it to something or someone else, is a humbling experience that requires true courage, vulnerability, faith, and generosity. All qualities I know you have acquired by now, qualities that have prepared you to take in the lessons you have learned to an all new level and to commit to satisfaction in every area of your life, without second-guessing for a moment whether or not you deserve everything you desire. You do. So, before you rush to turn the page and move into the support work, I call on you, *yes, you,* just as I called on Nina the day we had our uncomfortable conversation, to let my words reach you. Right now, in this *very moment,* hear me.

You deserve to end the diet cycle that has consumed you for so long. You are meant to be fit, to feel beautiful, and to nurture your incredible body. You were born worthy and you still are. This and only this, is the truth about who you are. Not the judgments of your pasts, not the fear of what could happen, not the painful things someone said or did to you, not even your losses or your mistakes. It's time you receive your truth fully.

That is why you were guided to pick up this book in the first place. If you remain willing to receive it, that truth that lives within you will continue to guide you and support you no matter what you desire in your life.

Now that you've just read that paragraph, don't let the voice in your head fool you, the voice that might be saying, "We've been through these concepts before. She wrote those same words over and over again. We've read them enough times. What's different here, in this step?"

You are. You are different. I am not asking you to write down my words or even remember them. I am asking you to receive them, to allow the truth I am called to share with you to reach past your rationality and make a permanent mark in the biology of your soul.

Now, are you ready to do that? I know, it's a lot to ask of you, but I hope you'll feel generous enough to let my words sink in deep, and stay with you forever.

P.S. In the next chapter, you'll see how simple it is to put all of the seven steps together and turn this process into a quick bounce back strategy that you can use at any time in your day to shift your perception and stick to your journey to *Free Your Body*. In less than fifteen minutes, I will show you how to remove the blocks that hold you back and return to a mindset that will inevitably attract the most amazing results in your body and in your life. But first, I have laid out for you the most effective practices to help you master the art of receiving, and I have no doubt that you will be nothing less than amazed at how incredible life gets to be, the moment you trust that you deserve all that you have always desired.

So, as tempting as it may be to move on and experience the power of all seven steps, do not skip the support work of this chapter. *Receive it.*

SUPPORT WORK

POWER STATEMENT

*Write down the following power statement
and repeat it as often as you can.*

"I choose to receive fully and safely."

Use this statement whenever you feel compelled to pull away from being vulnerable and fully expe-riencing the presence, kindness, love, and generosity of those around you. Please be mindful to practice this exercise only when surrounded by people you can trust. Pay special attention to the times you are holding yourself back from receiving, whether it is a gift, emotional support, assis-tance at work, a compliment, a meal, an orgasm, or even something as small as a smile from a stranger. Right there, stop whatever it is you are doing and recognize you have an opportunity to practice your Power Statement and strengthen your connection with your self and your body. Quickly repeat to your self or out loud: **"I choose to re-ceive fully and safely"**

YOUR FOUNDATION

Go back to page 192, copy down your Foundation Statement, then take five minutes to add to it any insights you have received from this chapter. Here are some examples: "I choose to believe it's safe to receive ", or "I choose to believe I am ready to receive fully and with grace.". Remember to take no more than five minutes to complete this exercise and write something that feels believable and good to you in this moment. Complete it now:

I choose to believe that I am

_____

_____

_____

Once you've written a statement that feels good to you, copy it down onto an index card, a piece of paper, or on your phone. Make sure you read it frequently, but at least once first thing in the morn-ing, and once last thing at night. My hope is that you make your foundation practice part of your Forever Fit and Free future, so that no matter where you go or what you experience, you will al-ways have something solid to fall back on.

TAKE ACTION

Eating — the healing power of pleasure.

Turn off all distraction, light a candle, set up the nicest dinner table for your self and seat down to enjoy your favorite meal making sure everything you need is right in front of you. Then take three clearing breaths, and set the intention to learn about yourself and fully experience pleasure from a meal like you have never done before.

Before taking your first bite, take a moment to admire the colors and the shapes of plate of food before you, then shift your attention to the aromas, trying to internalize the sensual information you receive from your nostrils and create a memory, so that later on you'll be able to recall it at will. After five breaths spent paying attention to the aromas alone, proceed to get a bite of food in your mouth and chew it thoroughly, focusing on the texture, the flavors and the feelings on your palate. Remember to continue practicing your guidelines, resting your hands on you lap and allowing yourself to take in the experience. Continue eating until you feel fully satisfied, then journal about your experience.

**Change is opening your arms to the love
and abundance around us.**

CHOOSE
TO REPEAT

I am so proud of you.

These are not just words. In fact, feeling proud doesn't quite cover it. I wish you could be right here by my side, to see the goosebumps on my skin and feel the buzz in my solar plexus. I would look straight into your eyes and tell you how humbled and moved I am by your courage. You made it through all the seven steps, and I know without a shadow of doubt, that you now possess all the principles and the tools you need to be on your own and allow your life to shape into an intentional path, which will guide you to become more and more of the woman you were always meant to be. In fact, I am sure that at this point you can begin to recognize that although food and body obsession have been abusive life-companions that kept you from experiencing your greatness, the moment you chose yourself and allowed the light to shine upon your wounds, they became doorways that led you to rediscover who you are, claim what you need, and demand what you deserve.

As we near the end of this book together, you should know that I am not expecting you to be in a state of total bliss and unshakable confidence. In fact, having been through the seven steps myself, and having guided countless women in this same process, I know that many of you may be wondering what the next move is going to be, or possibly feel concerned about keeping up on your own. Know that these feelings are totally normal. Remember, you are not trying to be perfect or fix the way you feel (or the way you look, for that matter); you are here to choose your true *Self* one moment at the time, release what doesn't serve you, restore your birthright to freedom, happiness, and satisfaction, and allow the divine guidance that supports us at all times to show you the way into your own unique path to live free. We are here to take one small step in the right direction after the next, and watch our desires come to life. Rest assured that however you feel and wherever you are now as you read these words, you are exactly where you need to be—and I am proud of you for standing there.

Now that I got that proud mama moment out of the way, this final chapter is where I will show you how to put the seven steps together and turn them into a practical and sustainable strategy to stay centered on your body success journey, and to keep improving your health and your body. It's the same strategy I use for myself, and the same exact one I have taught to all my clients.

Meet Rakel.

It was early September 2018, and I was getting ready to lead the last of a four-day instructor-training program, designed to teach a group of forty-four Italian fitness instructors how to incorporate resilience training into a variety of movement disciplines, to enhance their clients experience and optimize their benefits. Teaching resilience training has to be one of my absolute favorite things to do, but for some reason, on that last day, when I walked into the gorgeous open space inside a majestic renaissance building in Florence city center, I felt unexcited and uninspired. Everything was perfectly set up—the drawing board, the white candles, the chairs, the mats, the essential oils diffusing, the blankets, and even the yoga cushions, which for some reason were so damn hard to find in Tuscany—and still, I felt unsettled.

Uh…okay…well I know what I'm doing, I thought to myself. *I've spoken about these subjects so many times before. I know the outline by heart… I'll get through this and go home. Maybe I am just tired. I'll get through this… it's all good…I'll get through this… it's all good…*

It's as if I was reciting a mantra to tune me in and find some kind of an intention, to end that training in a meaningful way. But nothing. Seeing that it was time to start, I accepted my less than ideal state, took a deep breath, and whispered a prayer to myself.

"Help me feel inspired, help me share my truth, help me serve to my greatest ability."

Then, I opened the ancient, giant doors to welcome everyone into the space. As soon as I did, two of the participants, both of whom had recently completed my seven-week Forever Fit and Free program, came up to me to share how happy they were.

"I meant to tell you this on the first day, but you were so busy getting everything organized," Jessica said. "At fort-eight-years-old, thanks to you, I am in the best shape of my life! Yesterday, Erica and I saw our in-house nutritionist, and I found out that *without dieting* my BMI is now down twenty percent body fat. *Twenty percent*! Can you believe that? I feel incredible!"

"That's great," I politely responded, as I watched other instructors walk in and find their seats.

"Really, *Rakel*!" Now Erica was insisting I listen. "We are so thankful! Just over a year ago, when I took my first Fuel class and you asked us to use a personal intention for our work together, I clearly remember writing down that I wanted my body to be better at fifty years old, than it was when I was 20. I am not kidding—now it is! I look better than ever, and I can do things I have never dreamed of doing before. And it's all because of what you taught us. This stuff works! It's crazy powerful!"

"That is awesome," I tried my best smile. "Really... I'm happy for both of you."

The chatter in the room was growing.

"Ladies... please..." I said turning to address the entire class. "Try to keep your voice to a minimum. We'll be ready to start very soon. Go ahead and take a seat".

Jessica and Erica found their seats in the brightest side of the room, the same exact spots they had occupied for the entire training, right beside a monumental fresco of a battle scene that had recently been restored.

"I'll play some music for you," I said. "Take a moment to settle in, see how you feel, and set an intention for this final day of training."

I walked over to the window ledge, picked up my phone, and pressed play on "Rise Up" by Andra Day. Then, I turned my back to the room of students unpacking their notes, stretching their bodies, and (softly) chatting with one another.

I faced the sunlight, stood still, placed my right hand on my heart, and took a few slow, clearing breaths.

"I choose me, right now, as I am—exactly the way I feel," I whispered. "I trust that there is a reason why those two women just came up to me and showed me how easily I can still be triggered by body insecurity. I don't need to know what my BMI is these days. Whatever that might be, it does not define my worth—my worth is my birthright. It also does not define them. I forgive them for still being attached to the need to prove themselves. They are free to disregard my suggestions to stop measuring their bodies, just like I am free to decide how to feel about this experience and release all judgments. Most of all, I forgive my fearful reaction and I *choose me* instead. I know that each time I witness my feelings, I acknowledge them, and I choose myself over fear, I rewire my brain to create strong habits that support my desires. I choose to let this very lesson become fuel for the most incredible training I can deliver to this group. I know that whenever I show up, I am kept up. I asked for teaching inspiration for today and I received it—I am supported. All is well."

The song ended. I turned around and picked up the microphone.

"This morning is magical," I said, hearing the echo of my voice now amplified. "I walked in with a detailed outline to teach you how to help your clients break through the belief that something is too hard, too difficult, or even impossible to achieve. However, as I stand here before you, I feel called to address that same topic from a very personal prospective. You see, without you knowing it, for the duration of the song that I just played, four minutes and thirteen seconds, to be exact, I managed to do quite a few things that years ago I would have classified as extremely difficult—*impossible*."

I turned around and walked towards the large white board as I continued speaking.

"In that short time, I made seven powerful choices that were able to shift my perception and cause miraculous change within me and now without. These seven powerful choices are today's training, so get your journal out because I'm about to teach you a system what will shift your connection to your body, and to your life, forever."

I began to write the seven steps on the board, and instead of sharing perfectly crafted examples with each explanation, I walked the group through each step, using my own experience of making the shifts in four minutes and thirteen seconds.

1. Choose Me.

"As you all walked in, I witnessed myself being triggered by two women who innocently shared with me their excitement for seeing great results in their body and almost instantly I began to compare myself to them. When I caught my reaction, rather than judge myself for being triggered or pretend it never happened, I asked all of you to settle in while I turned around, play a song that always helps me connect to my truth, and said to myself, "I choose me.""

2. Choose Now.

"In that very moment, imperfect as it was, I honored myself. I connected to my own breath, and remembered that I am a woman who has no need to prove her worth or deny her feelings to do her job. I am a woman who knows she deserves to address her true needs at any given moment, no matter who is around her or what is at stake. My wellbeing and my self-worth gets to come first."

3. Choose to Trust.

"As I tuned into the moment, I began to open up to the great lesson I was receiving this morning. You see, when I first walked into this room, I was prepared to teach today's outline, but I felt disconnected and uninspired. Not in the least as excited as I normally feel when I get to share something I believe in so deeply, as I do about the importance of building resilience in our bodies and in our lives. So rather than resigning to the idea of getting through the day, I asked the Universe to give me something that could move me to my core, so that I could serve you from my most powerful truth. And sure enough, I received what I'd asked for. The moment I chose to trust, I recognized the trigger I experienced a few minutes ago, as the true gift that it was. An opportunity to reconnect, chose me, and have something practical, powerful, and exciting to teach you with the passion and conviction that you can now feel coming through my voice."

4. Choose to Forgive.

"Once I was clear on what I had been trigged by, I quickly forgave myself for doubting my own worth and judging my own students. If fact, I chose to release all judgments against all involved, so that I could rejoice in the lesson, experience gratitude, and determine the way it could serve me, as your teacher, the most."

5. Choose to Pause.

"Once I felt that release, instead of rushing back to the room and allowing the pressure of the day to take me away from being fully present to myself, I took a few extra moments to feel clear and witness my body open and void of emotional restraints. After a few long calming breaths, I began to settle into a deeper state of presence, until I felt completely grounded and relaxed."

6. Choose to Reset.

"Fully present to my newfound clarity, I chose to use what had just happened as an opportunity to make a new connection, between feeling triggered by someone commenting about their low body-fat percentage and *choosing myself* instead of my judgments, knowing that each time I do so, I strengthen my desire to honor myself above all things. Right there, I reminded myself that each time I practice choosing myself when I feel triggered by body insecurities, I get one step closer to making that choice an automatic response, one that will happen so fast, I won't even noticed being triggered in the first place."

7. Choose to Receive.

"Finally, as the song came to an end, I chose to take in the immense feeling of gratitude for the lesson that was offered to me. I chose to receive it fully and to allow myself to feel inspired by what had happened. I know, without a doubt—it was divine. Thanks to this brief, intense, challenging experience, I now have the most powerful example for the very topic I am here to teach you today—resilience training and *mindset for fitness.*"

'*Four minutes and thirteen seconds people*—you hear me?" I said after I finished explaining all seven choices. "That's how long it can take to shift your energy, connect with your body, reclaim your purpose, and show up fully for whatever it is you are called to do, when you are willing to choose yourself. Less than five minutes to get into your most powerful mindset— you can all do this!"

As soon as I said that, I quickly turned towards Jessica and Erika to assess their body language and evaluate whether or not I should say something to them. As much as I was concerned about the two women's feelings, I knew they had been on their Forever Fit and Free Journey for weeks, and thus I trusted they possessed the tools to process what was happening and allow the rest of the group to have a powerful learning experience. I wasn't wrong.

Jessica looked grounded and relaxed, her lips bearing the semblance of a soft and reassuring smile, and her hands resting gently on her open notebook. While Erika's eyes were fully lit up, as if a million new and brilliant ideas were streaming through her brain with excitement. Both women had just witnessed the very process they had been practicing for weeks coming full circle before their eyes and now they were just as eager as ever. In fact, I could sense a palpable readiness about them, which told me the honest outing of my feelings and my willingness to be vulnerable in front of my students had awakened within them, a desire to dive in even deeper into the work.

As for the rest of the women in the room, they got to spend the last day of training discussing what it truly means to *build our resilience muscle* and to be part of a conversation far more powerful than what I could have ever anticipated or planned. By the time we walked out that evening, I knew without a doubt, that everyone in the room had gained a visceral understanding that whenever an apparent obstacle presents itself, we don't need to ignore or escape it. We can pick up the pace to meet it half way, use it as fuel for our journey, whether that is to boost athletic performance, grow our inner confidence, or teach to a room full of strangers something we are passionate about, knowing in our heart that no matter its nature, a challenge can only truly happen through us—never to us.

Four minutes and thirteen seconds was all it took me to go through the seven steps and turn an uninspired day into an epic experience for all.

Now, let's say, for the sake of argument, that I wasn't prepared to make the call to place that group of women on hold, listen to my intuition, and decide to give myself a chance to work things out internally before starting that training. Let's say I kept it for myself, ignored my reaction or even turned it into resentment towards those two women in the group. *What do you think would have happened?*

Best case scenario, I would have gotten through my outline for the day and regurgitated a bunch of information without connecting for a moment with anyone in the room. I would have missed the opportunity to feel grateful toward Jessica and Erica, two students of mine that—without planning for it— came in that morning to be my teachers. Most importantly, everyone in the room would have missed the lesson I shared with them, which I know they were able to carry on to their students and those they love. And the best part of all, is that although in the very moment Jessica and Erica made those comments I felt like I was sinking in shame, jealousy, frustration and smallness, seven steps and only a few minutes later, I felt awesome and ready to rock the room, inspire others, and make a difference in their bodies and their lives.

That was probably one of the best training sessions I have taught to this day, and all thanks to one funky start that I *chose* to turn around—by going through the seven-step process I was guided to discover myself. That is why I encourage you to use this simple system as your daily go-to strategy to keep yourself on the right path to *Free Your Body*. Stay willing to practice it over and over again, and I promise, you will be able to turn yourself around in a matter of minutes—possibly under five—any time you need or want to. Want to hear about another example of how to put there seven steps together?

This email from my client Jamie says it all.

It always starts with the best of intentions. I leave my house with my computer, my workout bag, my journal, my clients' paperwork, my three children and their three backpacks, diaper change for the little one, snacks, water, cash, credit cards, phone charger, headphones, and my Fuel day mantra scheduled to appear on my phone at specific times during the day to remind me what I am actively working on this week—keep up and you will be kept up. I drop the kids at school, check with my mother-in-law to confirm pick-up time, grab coffee, get to the office early, respond to urgent emails and messages, and prepare for my first client. Holding a printout of my full day schedule in my hands, I feel empowered, organized and on top my life. I plan to see seven clients today, close two deals, and leave the office no later 6:45 PM so that I can come to your 7:30 PM Fuel class before heading home. However, somewhere between the hours of 8:00 AM and 6:00 PM, I realize that my good intentions and motivation for the evening have taken a different route. By the time the second deal doesn't close, and I get to end an inconclusive 40-minute phone conversation with my ever-complaining client, the last thing I want to do is change into workout gear and connect with my body. Suddenly, I'm thinking that it would be a shame not to take advantage of the fact the kids are at my mother-in-law's for dinner. I could... grab some food, go home, relax, and have a date night with Netflix to unwind from such a disappointing day. After all, nothing went as planned... I may as well call it the day. By the time I walk out of the office, I have made up my mind—I am going home. Defeated, yet relieved by having made a decision, I walk to my car, open the door, get in, turn on the engine, and then it comes — the voice within me, whispering, "Should I really go home? Am I tired, or is something else going on?" I realize in that moment that I am not interested in resting or taking a nap— all I want to do is disconnect from my life the best way I know how, by sitting on my sofa, TV on, and Chinese takeout neatly displayed on my coffee table, with no one around to see me or judge me. I start driving, still determined to go home, but I tell myself: 'just drive by the studio and see how you feel'. I want to be at peace and own my choice whatever that is. I anticipate a quick drive by, because parking is always an issue in your area, but once I get there, I notice an open parking spot right in front of the entrance door. Disappointed, I park my car, turn off the engine, and sit in stillness staring at my hands resting on the steering wheel. The choice gets real: "What's it gonna be?" I could go home to disconnect or walk inside and engage with myself. Every muscle in my body does NOT want to move, yet I witness myself getting out the car, my hands grabbing the mat from the trunk, and my feet hesitantly moving one step in front of the other until finally, I realize that I've walked through the door. Out loud, I tell myself "Ok... I got you. I Choose You." Upstairs, fully changed into my workout gear, I enter the candle lit studio and in one second, I realize the hardest part of my day is over. The energy of the room feels warm and supporting— for today, I have won. The class hasn't even started yet, but I know I have already done my work by showing up. Next thing I see is you, walking towards me to say hello and hug me the way you know how to hug, leaving no room for holding back or hiding anything from you. I feel resistant to receive your warm welcome at first, then I give in, and my chest expands and opens up together with yours as I hear you say, 'It's so great you made it'. A few moments later the class starts, a pose leads to another, a movement merges into the next, and a little over fifty minutes later I feel sweaty, tired, and one with myself and everyone in the room. Everything is released—my muscles, my spine, my doubts, my need to escape, the deals I didn't close, my emotional hunger, my fatigue, my obsessive thoughts about my ex-husband, my resistance, my breath, and my whole skeletal structure—released into the ground. I am free, and I feel powerful.

Thank you,
Jamie

Jamie's willingness to revisit her process, to question her intentions, and to take one tiny step in the right direction after another guided her to choose herself, no matter how imperfect her day turned out to be. Her story shows us that as much as we love and welcome big accomplishments and productive days, the times we are able to choose ourselves when things don't go the way we planned, are the moments that allow us to shift our energy in the most powerful ways. These are the times that teach us the very core message of *Free Your Body*—that there is no need to fix anything in us or around us. All it takes is being willing to choose ourselves and take one small right action, which will inevitably lead us into the next.

In fact, what's most powerful about Jamie's example, isn't the fact she was able to show up for her workout routine no matter what her day looked like. It's the reason *why* she did it. Her choice did not come from the desire to push herself to do "whatever it takes" to get in shape, maintain her commitment, or burn those few hundred calories per day, no matter what happened at work. Instead she kept her commitment to choose herself through a willingness to see what happens if she stayed present to her feelings and followed her intuition one step at a time, without seeking control.

Her experience is a testament that long-lasting change comes thanks to small and consistent right actions taken in the present moment. If you can't exercise one day, then choose to park your car few blocks away, take the stairs, play music and dance around in your house, or go for a walk on your lunch break. No, you won't burn *as many* calories as if you attended a hot yoga class followed by a full session of strength training, but that 20-minute walk you took before dinner will always be more effective than the 10 miles you never got to run.

When I next saw Jamie for a private session, we spoke about the email she sent me.

"What an awesome moment," she said. "I got to see for myself how the process truly works—literally one step after the other. But…"

"But what?" I asked.

"I just don't know what's next. Is there another step now?"

"Well, all you have to do now is choose to keep up with the process… continue to choose yourself, choose now, choose …"

"Wait—" She stopped me mid-sentence. "Do you mean do all the work all over again… *all seven steps?*"

"Yes, and no. *Yes*, you need to continue to choose yourself, choose now, to trust, to forgive, to pause, to reset and to receive. And *no*, the seven steps will never be the same again because you are no longer the same. Each time you make those choices about any event or around any circumstance, you will be a little freer, stronger, clearer, and better prepared to make this process your own. In no time, it will become second nature, a part of you, not a burden, and never a to-do list. All you have to do is keep up with it and keep making choices that honor you, and you will be supported."

Jamie looked at me, nodded her head, and said nothing. But everything about her, from her proud posture, to the firm look I saw in her eyes, reveled to me she possessed all the understanding she needed to be fit and free, forever. All she had to do now, was keep up with her commitment.

Keep up and you will be kept up,
— Yogi Bhajan

THE WORK WORKS WHEN YOU WORK IT

The expression, "to keep," originates from Latin conservare, which means *to preserve, keep safe* and tenere, *to keep, retain*. We know by now that each time we repeat an action, we create a neuropath in our brain that supports it, and that eventually, with enough repetition, that action becomes an automatic response which bypasses decision making—we call that a habit. That's what I hope choosing your *Self* has become for you at this point, a powerful habit you will choose to safeguard and retain at all costs. There is only one way to do that; Repeat it again and again.

There is something powerful that happens when we keep showing up for ourselves over time, something that is not easy to explain but is none the less real and palpable to all who have found themselves present to that momentum, where things begin to flow more effortlessly and life gets suddenly real groovy. It is almost as if the Universe takes notice of our commitment, acknowledges our efforts, and decides to back us up in powerful ways.

If you are familiar with Kundalini Yoga, then you have probably heard the mantra "Keep up and you will be kept up," which Yogi Bhajan used to remind his students that the path to mastery takes persistence. I am sure there are many ways to interpret his message, but to me, it means that once we show up for ourselves and do what we can in the moment, the universe moves in to support us. In other words, when we align with our desires and maintain momentum by taking small consistent right actions, life starts to conspire with us, and to support us in miraculous ways.

I don't believe it was a coincidence that once Jamie decided to drive by the studio, she found a parking spot right in front of the entrance door, (especially considering parking at that time is impossible) and that once she made the effort to walk inside, she found a warm candle lit room ready to welcome her and support her through her practice. Her willingness allowed the universe to conspire with her and support her all the way through.

In the same way, when you picked up this book, chose to read it, and decided to incorporate the seven-step teaching into your life, you made a powerful choice to honor yourself and initiate a transformational journey. Weather you were aware of it or not, that very first moment you chose yourself, life stopped happening to you, and began happening through you. You began to come before your desires, before your judgments, before your life circumstances, and before your old stories, and that right there, changed everything. All you need to do at this point, is keep putting together the seven steps, continue moving forward, turn around any situation that doesn't serve you, and make this practice as effortless as possible.

Listen, I know how overwhelming this can appear at first, but I promise you, it is totally doable. In fact, I am determined to tear away any doubt you may still have, to make sure at the end of this last chapter you feel prepared and empowered to be on your own. So here is another tangible example of how one of my clients used the seven-step process to shift a challenging life situation into a miraculous opportunity for growth in only a few minutes.

Meet Heleen.

Heleen couldn't wait to attend her yearly yoga retreat in Costa Rica. She had booked a single superior room overlooking the ocean and she was ready to unwind and relax after one of the most stressful years in her entire career. However, a week before her departure, she received an email from the host—a yoga teacher she had followed and looked up to for years—asking her if she'd be so kind to share her room with a young woman who had joined the retreat at the last minute. Heleen had been looking forward to enjoying some alone time all year, but faced by the urgency to respond and feeling guilty for turning down a personal request from someone she admired greatly, she politely agreed. Her roommate Janice was a lovely person—warm, gracious, and very sweet. She was also young, beautiful, sensual, and extremely comfortable in her perfectly toned, thin body, which triggered Heleen's old habit of comparing herself to other women around her, which left her feeling depressed and inadequate.

Stressed out and ashamed by her feelings, Heleen spent the first two days in Costa Rica eating and drinking well beyond what her body desired and skipping out on the very things she had been looking forward to—connecting with herself and practicing yoga in her favorite natural setting on the planet. On the third day however, she remembered she had a choice. Heleen walked to the ocean, sat down under the shade of a palm tree, and opened her journal to a brand-new, blank page.

I choose me.

She wrote the words right at the top. Instantly, she felt a little relief, if anything because she remembered she had something to fall back on, a system to realign and a strategy to return to what felt right for her. Then, she took a next step and decided to use the journaling prompt I gave her in one of our sessions to help her combine all seven steps on her daily life. (By the way, this is the same exact journal prompt you can find in the resource section of this book.)

With her permission, straight out of her journal, here is how Heleen worked her seven steps.

Step 1— Choose you:

A. What are the old points of reference —the limiting beliefs coming to play in this situation?: *'She is better than you'*, *'She has it all and you have nothing.'*, *' You don't matter.'*, *'You will never get the attention you want.'*, *'You are insignificant.'*, *'You are destined to be fat and ugly.'* *'You are old and undesirable'*.

B. Align your beliefs with your desire. What do you know for certain about yourself that can help you elevate your energy now? *I believe that I am resilient, and I know deep in my heart I can overcome any challenge that comes my way. I have done it before. I can do it again. My worth is my birthright. I am more than these negative thoughts and opinions and I have worked long enough on myself and my relationship to my body to know how to bounce back and turn things around.*

C. Do you have a choice other than escape or ignore what is happening in this moment? Anything you can do now that can make you feel even a little bit better? *I do. Just because I had two terrible days, I don't need to make this a terrible week. I can choose. I can either indulge in feeling ugly, fat, old, and envious, and tell myself that I am a bad person, that I don't belong here, or I can choose myself. It's not too late. I have agreed to share the room, but it's not working out for me. I am not trapped. I am not a prisoner. I am not a child. I am willing to be vulnerable and express my needs to others. Restoring my sense of wellbeing and connection is my responsibility to myself and it is mine alone.*

Step 2 — Choose Now:

What reason do you have now to be happy? *I'm in Costa Rica in a beautiful resort, the weather is perfect, the sun is shining, I have a stunning view from my balcony. I am healthy. I am thirty-five pounds lighter than last year. I have been off medications for eight months. My feet are getting tanned. I get to do sunset yoga this evening. I am facing my fears. I am responsible for myself and it feels damn good. I know how to choose me and express my needs. I may have been triggered, but I've got the tools to process what happened and restore my sense of wellbeing.*

Step 3 — Choose to Trust:

What is happening? Can you face it and find the lesson in it? *It's so clear to me right now. I have been too concerned with fitting in. I wanted everyone here to think highly of me, see me as someone spiritual. I didn't want them to know how fragile I truly am, how vulnerable and how small I feel at times. This is an opportunity to honor my truth and bring forth a meaningful experience for everyone. I feel called to share what*

I feel with others and I want to stand up to reclaim the space I need. I am ready to speak up.

Step 4— Choose to Forgive.

In which way can you forgive yourself? *I forgive myself for wanting to impress people. I forgive myself for feeling envious and uncomfortable around younger, beautiful women. I've been her age, and I am so much happier now. I forgive myself for what I ate and drank these past two days and for missing out on the retreat all together. Most of all, I forgive myself for not listening to my intuition about needing my own room and feeling free to say no from the beginning.*

Step 5 — Choose to Pause.

In which way have you progressed and what have you learned along the way? *OMG... Only being able to know there is another way to live and feeling worthy enough to consider standing up for myself is nothing short of a miracle for me.*

Step 6 — Choose to Reset.

In which way can you reset your brain to create new supporting habits for yourself? *I know that when I feel trapped and think I have no choices, I can choose myself and make that a habit. It's already so much easier than it used to be. I also know that when I feel pressured into doing something that doesn't feel completely right, I can get in the habit of pausing and give myself enough time to better evaluate my options. I am committed to get in a place in my life where saying "let me think about it" becomes an automatic response no matter who is asking.*

Step 7 — Choose to Receive.

What can you gain from this experience? How can this moment impact your life in a powerful way and serve you the most? *This is what I have asked for— transformation—that is what I have gotten. Now I can just receive this lesson, take action, ask for what I need, and witness my growth.*

Journaling through the seven steps under a palm tree on a beach took Heleen no more than fifteen minutes, after which she got up feeling clear and ready to take what felt like the next right action. She participated in a beautiful session of sunset yoga, and before the group met for dinner, she asked the host teacher if they could speak in private for a moment.

"I am sorry, but I can't do this." Heleen took a deep breath. "I can't share my room anymore."

"Did something happen?" The host looked surprised. "I thought you and Janice went along just fine."

"It has nothing to do with Janice and all to do with me," Heleen said. "When you asked me to share my room I said yes, but only because I didn't want to disappoint you."

The teacher looked even more surprised but continued listening.

"Please... you must know that I take full responsibility for all of that. However, for the first time in my life, I know I need to choose myself and honor what feels right for me. Sharing my room when I need space to be alone is not what I need in my life right now. I hate to cause you any trouble, but this is something important I have to do for me, and I will not turn my back on myself again."

The host teacher was left with no choice. She wasn't terribly happy about it, but nonetheless she stepped up and took responsibility for her group by sharing her own room with Janice, thus giving Heleen the opportunity to regain her own space and feel immensely proud of herself.

But that wasn't all that happened. Over the next few days Heleen felt so inspired by her newfound ability to choose herself, that she shared her humbling experience with the entire group of twenty-six women, whom courageously, following her example, took their turn and shared how comparison to other women's bodies had always effected their lives and limited their yoga practice. Thanks to her willingness to choose herself, to grab her journal, to walk to the ocean, to sit down to write her way through each step of the process, receive the lesson, stand up to face the host, and openly share her feelings, Heleen gave everyone the opportunity to learn from her experience and take home something far more valuable than a cute souvenir handcrafted in Santa Teresa beach—a beam of her courage, which I am sure ended up healing more than just her own wounds.

Whether you feel that journaling your way through the seven steps like Heleen did is your thing, or like me, you get used to mentally going through the whole process in your head wherever you are—including a room full of people— each time you say to yourself, *I choose me,* you get to reset your forever fit and free journey in motion. That first choice is the decision that cuts off all other possibilities. It's the willingness to see things differently, to understand what is holding you back, to raise above old stories, to tune in, to feel, to forgive, to pause, to acknowledge how far you have come, and finally, to receive the lesson that is bestowed upon you. There is no way to do it wrong, except not doing it or trying to be perfect at it. And no, there is no way to do the work without being uncomfortable at times. The good news is, the more you practice the more you will be able to welcome the process into your life—you will see it for what it truly is—a powerful yet practical strategy to rise above life circumstances and meet your challenge halfway.

SEAL YOUR ALLIANCE

So now that you know how to put it all together, it's time to seal your commitment to be free in your own body, so that you can take a first, powerful step on your own. To do that, I have created a simple contract that I encourage you to fill out and sign *right away.* Seriously, *do not wait a moment longer!* Think of this contract as a way to formalize your agreement between your desires, your beliefs, and your actions, knowing that by consolidating your alliance in writing, you make it effective and real. In fact, studies show that creating and signing a written agreement, whether with ourselves or someone else, increases the likelihood of fulfilling our commitment over time.

So here it is, your formal commitment to Choose You. Drop into your body fully, set an intention, and get ready to seal your own alliance.

You can complete the contract right here in the book or download a copy at www.rakelchafir.com/bookresources.

I, _____ , Choose Me, Now, As I Am. I know times will come when I will fall, relapse, breakdown, or forget, and in those times, I will forgive myself, acknowledge my experience, and see it as an opportunity to Choose Me above all things, strengthen my connection to the present moment, reaffirm my faith in the process, and pause to remember I am more than any endearing quality or imperfection, achievement or failure, judgment or opinion—including my own.

I will keep in mind that each time I honor my body and choose myself, I am rewiring my brain and optimizing my ability to receive my deepest desires, including the ability to be forever fit.

I hereby agree to invest the next forty days in following the guidelines to the best of my abilities, as well as practice the seven step forever fit and free process whenever I see an opportunity, but at least once per day. In addition, I commit to look for progress and not perfection in my practice. In the event I forget about the guidelines or put them aside for a period of time, I pledge to remember that all I have to do is choose again, start over with the forty-day period, without judging myself or feeling distressed.

By signing this contract I agree to make a daily effort to re-member that I am the Angel in the stone, and my life purpose is not to fix the outer layers that cover her up, but rather take one step at the time, so that layer after layer, I can set her free.

Date:_____/_____/_____
Signature_____

"What will happen after forty days?" you may ask. As you learned in Chapter 2, Choose Now, and don't worry about it. The answer will be available within you after you complete your practice time.

With Love,
Rakel

CONCLUSION

I will leave you with this: Even when it feels like you have no choice, you still can choose. In the third chapter of this book, I shared with you how much I struggled to finally embrace my calling fully and take the inspired action to write a book, to share with the world a path that has led me—and many other women—to freedom from food and body obsession. I'd like to end this part of our journey together going back there, to those moments when my writing adventure first started and when I had to make a choice to either go for it or not.

It was much more than saying yes to a book. It was saying yes to myself. Saying, 'yes your message is important. Your voice must be heard. Your truth is powerful and worth sharing. You are worthy just as you are.' which is the very core message within this book process and the reason why this method works like no other does.

When I finished the first draft of the first chapter of this book, I experienced a profound sense of empowerment. I felt excited and proud of myself—confident I was on the right path and that I could finally look at my life experiences as a whole, understanding the unfolding of the lessons I had to learn so that now I could be ready to teach them to many. That day, with a nine-page document I saved on my desktop as 'My book,' I felt full and complete. That day, I sat down to eat at regular meal times, and there was no desire for anything other than nurturing my body. No feelings to shut down, no compulsion to reward myself, and no punishment for self-expression. *This is it! This is what I am meant to do!* I told myself, curious of the strong and peaceful state I experienced deep inside my body. You see, the old me would have stressed out about Chapters 2, 3, 4, 5 and so on. She would have reminded herself that she had no title, no precise outline, no editor, agent, publisher, or writing degree, and there couldn't possibly be anything worth celebrating in nine written pages (which by the way, never actually ended up making it into the book you just read). And yet, with that one small action of starting my book, I felt complete.

That day I couldn't wait to share what I wrote with my husband, so much so that I quickly emailed the beginning of my book to him without much hesitation. My husband has always been my greatest cheerleader, so I expected him to be enthusiastic and moved by what I wrote, maybe even more than I was. A few hours went by, and I saw no response from him. I called him and asked him if he had a chance to read it. "Yes," he answered. "Let's talk about it when I get home." That was not the answer I expected. I hung up the phone, waited restlessly for five long minutes, then I called him back demanding he share his opinion as if my life depended on it.

Hesitantly, Alex told me "the book" was well-written, but he didn't feel the stories I chose to narrate were particularly interesting. He felt that I described myself as weak and fragile, rather than the vibrant and charismatic person I am in real life. But when he told me other women wouldn't be inspired by someone so broken, I felt wounded at my core. A knife cutting straight through my chest would have been soothing compared to what I experienced listening to my husband point out his thoughts about some of the most vulnerable moments of my childhood.

"Of course, I sounded like the looser victim, that is exactly how I felt!" I shouted.

After calling him an insensitive asshole, I hung up the phone feeling once more defeated, judged, and packed with rage. Who was I kidding? No one ever got me, and no one will ever get me. I am alone, unlikable, unlovable, and destined to be hurt by others—even by my husband. My real self isn't likable or respectable. I have no talent and none of my stories are relevant or interesting! Let's just kill this book idea at once. I don't know how I ever got the audacity to think I could be doing this anyway.

Pause. Heartbeat. Breath. The inner voice comes just in time.

"Choose…" then silence. "Choose… you know that is all you have to do."

And so, I did. With a hand on my heart and my eyes closed I said yes to my purpose and promised myself to continue saying yes until the very last page.

"I choose to believe *I am always guided*. I choose to believe *I am more than my fear* and even this hurtful episode had to happen to test how serious I am about moving forward and how willing I am to stand tall on my own for what I believe in. My message may not be for everyone, it may not move my husband, but there are countless women like me out there, women who need to hear that they are not alone and that they too can make a choice that can set them free.

I let go of my attachment to the outcome, and I choose to trust that I am guided. I know the desire that burns deep within my body is there to be expressed. My truth will heal many as it is healing me now. Making my husband my savior is giving him a role that I am to fulfill on my own. I am my own savior. The story of the defenseless girl who suffered the heartbreaking criticism from her father doesn't need to be projected upon others any longer. I am not defenseless or better, I don't have any good reasons to defend myself—my worth is my birthright and I choose me as many times as I need to, for as long as I need to.

I choose to forgive myself and I choose to forgive Alex *(although trust me, there is no way I'll share with him another page of this book until it's ready to be published)*. I choose to be present to each word, each sentence, each chapter, until someday I'll get to the last page and realize I just wrote the end to my book."

That's where we are right now, and all I can do is feel proud of me and you both. My wish is that somehow my words will resonate with you and help you find or deepen your commitment to yourself, your body, and your life purpose. You see, I may not know you personally, but I do know for certain that you deserve to be free and to feel confident forever. By now you should know that too.

May the relationship with food and body image that has caused years of anguish and self-denial become the door that will open a path of love, fulfillment, and spiritual awareness.

Remember, each moment you get to choose yourself, you have already won. And just like that, in this very moment, as I write the last sentence of the final chapter of a book that hasn't yet been read by anyone other than my editor, I know in my heart, I have already won. I am full.

Now you go, keep up and trust you will be kept up.

ACKNOWLEDGMENTS

Thank you to my husband Alex, for standing by my side during some of the most difficult years of my life and for encouraging me to be the change I want to see in the world! Without you, so much of what I do would not be possible. To my mother in law Gina, for taking care of the boys so I could have time to write and connect with myself. What a journey this has been! Thank you to my editor and friend, Janna Hockenjos. Your unconditional support, guidance, and faith in my message helped me understand that writing a book is not only a massive project to bring to life but a personal healing journey. Thank you Gabby Bernstein for reawakening faith in myself and the universe and Katie Karas for all the guidance and support you offered me over the years. So much love goes to my clients! Thank you for your willingness to grow into the women you were always meant to be. I love you.

A huge shout-out to my Spirit Junkies' family! You make me feel seen, understood, and loved for who I really am. For that, I'll be forever grateful. Finally thank you to my beautiful children, William and Donovan, for teaching me unconditional love and inspiring me to show up each and every day to heal, grow, and be the best human I can be. You are my everything.

ABOUT THE AUTHOR

Rakel Chafir is a body confidence expert and success coach who teaches women how to heal their relationship with their body so they can reach their full potential in life. Her signature approach combines physical movement, resilience training and spiritual principles to help clients let go of unwanted weight, eliminate addictive behaviors, and more.

Rakel has worked in some of New York City's most elite studios as a certified personal trainer and also has an extensive background in health, wellness that includes being the founder of Fuel -The Body Resilience Training, a Master Expert in Hypopressive Abdominal Method, and more. Her expertise has been featured on *Thrive Global, Best Self Media, Positively Positive, She Owns It, CEOWorld Magazine, and Addicted2Success*.

www.rakelchafir.com

Made in the USA
Middletown, DE
15 November 2020

23941333R00163